PUFFIN BOOKS

The Diary of a Killer Cat

Anne Fine was born and educated in the Midlands, and now lives in County Durham. She has written numerous highly acclaimed and prize-winning books for children and adults.

Her novel *The Tulip Touch* won the Whitbread Children's Book of the Year Award; *Goggle-Eyes* won the *Guardian* Children's Fiction Award and the Carnegie Medal, and was adapted for television by the BBC; *Flour Babies* won the Carnegie Medal and the Whitbread Children's Book Award; *Bill's New Frock* won a Smarties Prize, and *Madame Doubtfire* has become a major feature film starring Robin Williams.

www.annefine.co.uk

Other books by Anne Fine

Books for younger readers

Care of Henry
Countdown
Design-a-Pram
The Haunting of Pip Parker
Jennifer's Diary
Only a Show
Press Play
Roll Over Roly
The Same Old Story Every Year
Scaredy-Cat
Stranger Danger?
The Worst Child I Ever Had

Books for middle-range readers

The Angel of Nitshill Road
Anneli the Art Hater
Bill's New Frock
The Chicken Gave It To Me
The Country Pancake
Crummy Mummy and Me
How to Write Really Badly
A Pack of Liars
A Sudden Glow of Gold
A Sudden Puff of Glittering Smoke
A Sudden Swirl of Icy Wind

Books for older readers

The Book of the Banshee
Flour Babies
Goggle-Eyes
The Granny Project
Madame Doubtfire
The Other Darker Ned
Round Behind the Ice-house
Step by Wicked Step
The Stone Menagerie
The Summer House Loon
The Tulip Touch

ANNE FINE

The Diary of a
Killer Cat

Illustrated by Steve Cox

PUFFIN BOOKS

PUFFIN BOOKS

Published by the Penguin Group
Penguin Books Ltd, 80 Strand, London WC2R 0RL, England
Penguin Putnam Inc., 375 Hudson Street, New York, New York 10014, USA
Penguin Books Australia Ltd, 250 Camberwell Road, Camberwell, Victoria 3124, Australia
Penguin Books Canada Ltd, 10 Alcorn Avenue, Toronto, Ontario, Canada M4V 3B2
Penguin Books India (P) Ltd, 11 Community Centre, Panchsheel Park, New Delhi – 110 017, India
Penguin Books (NZ) Ltd, Cnr Rosedale and Airborne Roads, Albany, Auckland, New Zealand
Penguin Books (South Africa) (Pty) Ltd, 24 Sturdee Avenue, Rosebank 2196, South Africa

Penguin Books Ltd, Registered Offices: 80 Strand, London WC2R 0RL, England

www.penguin.com

First published by Hamish Hamilton 1994
Published in Puffin Books 1996
1

Text copyright © Anne Fine, 1994
Illustrations copyright © Steve Cox, 1994
All rights reserved

The moral right of the author and illustrator has been asserted

Set in Baskerville

Printed in England by Clays Ltd, St Ives plc

British Library Cataloguing in Publication Data
A CIP catalogue record for this book is available from the British Library

This edition printed for Bradford and Bingley plc

ISBN 0–141–31582–2

1 : *Monday*

OKAY, OKAY. So hang me. I killed the bird. For pity's sake, I'm a *cat*. It's practically my *job* to go creeping round the garden after sweet little eensy-weensy birdy-pies that can hardly fly from one hedge to another. So what am I supposed to do when one of the poor feathery little flutterballs just about throws itself into my mouth? I mean, it practically landed on my paws. It could have *hurt* me.

Okay, *okay*. So I biffed it. Is that any reason for Ellie to cry in my fur so hard I almost *drown*, and squeeze me so hard I almost *choke?*

"Oh, Tuffy!" she says, all sniffles
and red eyes and piles of wet tissues.
"Oh, Tuffy. How could you *do* that?"

How could I *do* that? I'm a *cat.* How
did I know there was going to be such
a giant great fuss, with Ellie's mother
rushing off to fetch sheets of old

newspaper, and Ellie's father filling a bucket with soapy water?

Okay, *okay*. So maybe I shouldn't have dragged it in and left it on the carpet. And maybe the stains won't come out, ever.

So *hang* me.

2: *Tuesday*

I QUITE ENJOYED the little funeral. I don't think they really wanted me to come, but, after all, it's just as much my garden as theirs. In fact, I spend a whole lot more time in it than they do. I'm the only one in the family who uses it properly.

Not that they're grateful. You ought to hear them.

"That cat is *ruining* my flower beds. There are hardly any of the petunias left."

"I'd barely *planted* the lobelias before it was lying on top of them, squashing

4

them flat."

"I *do* wish it wouldn't dig holes in the anemones."

Moan, moan, moan, moan. I don't know why they bother to keep a cat, since all they ever seem to do is complain.

All except Ellie. She was too busy being soppy about the bird. She put it in a box, and packed it round with cotton wool, and dug a little hole, and then we all stood round it while she said a few words, wishing the bird luck in heaven.

"Go away," Ellie's father hissed at me. (I find that man quite rude.) But I just flicked my tail at him. Gave him the blink. Who does he think he is? If I want to watch a little birdy's funeral, I'll watch it. After all, I've known the bird longer than any of them have. I knew it when it was *alive*.

3: *Wednesday*

SO SPANK ME! I brought a dead mouse into their precious house. I didn't even kill it. When I came across it, it was already a goner. Nobody's safe around here. This avenue is ankle-deep in rat poison, fast cars charge up and down at all hours, and I'm not the only cat around here. I don't even know what happened to the thing. All I know is, I found it. It was already dead. (Fresh dead, but dead.) And at the time I thought it was a good idea to bring it home. Don't ask me why. I must have been crazy. How did I know that Ellie

7

was going to grab me and give me one of her little talks?

"Oh, Tuffy! That's the second time this week. I can't bear it. I know you're a cat, and it's natural and everything. But please, for my sake, stop."

She gazed into my eyes.

"Will you stop? Please?"

I gave her the blink. (Well, I tried. But she wasn't having any.)

"I *mean* it, Tuffy," she told me. "I love you, and I understand how you feel. But you've got to stop doing this, okay?"

She had me by the paws. What could I say? So I tried to look all sorry. And then she burst into tears all over again, and we had another funeral.

This place is turning into Fun City. It really is.

8

4: *Thursday*

OKAY, OKAY! I'll try and explain about
the rabbit. For starters, I don't think
anyone's given me enough credit for
getting it through the cat-flap. That
was *not easy*. I can tell you, it took
about an hour to get that rabbit
through that little hole. That rabbit
was downright *fat*. It was more like a
pig than a rabbit, if you want my
opinion.

Not that any of them cared what I
thought. They were going mental.

"It's Thumper!" cried Ellie. "It's
next-door's Thumper!"

"Oh, Lordy!" said Ellie's father. "Now we're in trouble. What are we going to do?"

Ellie's mother stared at me.

"How could a cat *do* that?" she asked. "I mean, it's not like a tiny bird, or a mouse, or anything. That rabbit is the same size as Tuffy. They both weigh a *ton*."

Nice. Very nice. This is my *family*, I'll have you know. Well, Ellie's family. But you take my point.

And Ellie, of course, freaked out. She went berserk.

"It's horrible," she cried. "*Horrible*. I can't believe that Tuffy could have done that. Thumper's been next door for years and years and years."

Sure. Thumper was a friend. I knew him well.

She turned on me.

"Tuffy! This is the end. That poor, poor rabbit. Look at him!"

And Thumper did look a bit of a mess, I admit it. I mean, most of it was only mud. And a few grass stains, I suppose. And there were quite a few bits of twig and stuff stuck in his fur. And he had a streak of oil on one ear. But no one gets dragged the whole way across a garden, and through a hedge, and over another garden, and through a freshly-oiled cat-flap, and ends up looking as if they're just off to a party.

And Thumper didn't care what he looked like. He was *dead*.

The rest of them minded, though. They minded a *lot*.

"What are we going to do?"

"Oh, this is dreadful. Next-door will never speak to us again."

"We must think of something."

And they did. I have to say, it was a brilliant plan, by any standards. First, Ellie's father fetched the bucket again, and filled it with warm soapy water. (He gave me a bit of a look as he did this, trying to make me feel guilty for the fact that he'd had to dip his hands in the old Fairy Liquid twice in one week. I just gave him my old 'I-am-not-impressed' stare back.)

Then Ellie's mother dunked Thumper in the bucket and gave him a nice bubbly wash and a swill-about. The water turned a pretty nasty brown colour. (All that mud.) And then, glaring at me as if it were all *my* fault, they tipped it down the sink and began over again with fresh soap suds.

Ellie was snivelling, of course.

"Do stop that, Ellie," her mother said. "It's getting on my nerves. If you

want to do something useful, go and
fetch the hairdrier."

So Ellie trailed upstairs, still bawling
her eyes out.

I sat on the top of the dresser, and
watched them.

They up-ended poor Thumper and
dunked him again in the bucket.
(Good job he wasn't his old self. He'd
have hated all this washing.) And
when the water finally ran clear, they
pulled him out and drained him.

15

Then they plonked him on newspaper, and gave Ellie the hairdrier.

"There you go," they said. "Fluff him up nicely."

Well, she got right into it, I can tell you. That Ellie could grow up to be a real hot-shot hairdresser, the way she fluffed him up. I have to say, I never saw Thumper look so nice before, and he lived in next-door's hutch for years and years, and I saw him every day.

"Hiya, Thump," I'd sort of nod at him as I strolled over the lawn to check out what was left in the feeding bowls further down the avenue.

"Hi, Tuff," he'd sort of twitch back.

Yes, we were good mates. We were pals. And so it was really nice to see him looking so spruced up and smart when Ellie had finished with him.

17

He looked *good*.

"What now?" said Ellie's father.

Ellie's mum gave him a look – the sort of look she sometimes gives me, only nicer.

"Oh, no," he said. "Not me. Oh, no, no, no, no, no."

"It's you or me," she said. "And I can't go, can I?"

"Why not?" he said. "You're smaller than I am. You can crawl through the hedge easier."

That's when I realised what they had in mind. But what could I say? What could I do to stop them? To *explain*?

Nothing. I'm just a cat.

I sat and watched.

5: Friday

I CALL IT Friday because they left it so
late. The clock was already well past
midnight by the time Ellie's father
finally heaved himself out of his comfy
chair in front of the telly and went
upstairs. When he came down again he
was dressed in black. Black from head
to foot.

"You look like a cat burglar," said
Ellie's mother.

"I wish someone would burgle *our*
cat," he muttered.

I just ignored him. I thought that
was best.

Together they went to the back
door.

"Don't switch the outside light on,"
he warned her. "You never know who
might be watching."

I tried to sneak out at the same time,
but Ellie's mother held me back with
her foot.

"You can just stay inside tonight,"
she told me. "We've had enough
trouble from you this week."

Fair's fair. And I heard all about it anyway, later, from Bella and Tiger and Pusskins. They all reported back. (They're good mates.) They all saw Ellie's father creeping across the lawn, with his plastic bag full of Thumper (wrapped nicely in a towel to keep him clean). They all saw him forcing his way through the hole in the hedge, and crawling across next-door's lawn on his tummy.

"Couldn't think *what* he was doing," Pusskins said afterwards.

"*Ruined* the hole in the hedge," complained Bella. "He's made it so big that the Thompson's rottweiler could get through it now."

"That father of Ellie's must have the most dreadful night vision," said Tiger. "It took him forever to find that hutch in the dark."

"And prise the door open."

"And stuff in poor old Thumper."

"And set him out neatly on his bed of straw."

"All curled up."

"With the straw patted up round him."

"So it looked as if he was sleeping."

"It was very, very lifelike," said Bella. "It could have fooled me. If anyone just happened to be passing in the dark, they'd really have thought that poor old Thumper had just died happily and peacefully in his sleep, after a good life, from old age."

They all began howling with laughter.

"Sshh!" I said. "Keep it down, guys. They'll hear, and I'm not supposed to be out tonight. I'm grounded."

They all stared at me.

"Get away with you!"

"Grounded?"

"What *for*?"

"Murder," I said. "For cold-blooded bunnicide."

That set us all off again. We yowled and yowled. The last I heard before we took off in a gang up Beechcroft Drive was one of the bedroom windows being flung open, and Ellie's father yelling, "How did you get out, you crafty beast?"

So what's he going to do? Nail up the cat-flap?

6: Still Friday

HE NAILED UP the cat-flap. Would you *believe* this man? He comes down the stairs this morning, and before he's even out of his pyjamas he's set to work with the hammer and a nail.

Bang, bang, bang, bang!

I'm giving him the stare, I really am. But then he turns round and speaks to me directly.

"There," he says. "That'll fix you. Now it swings *this* way – " He gives the cat-flap a hefty shove with his foot. "But it doesn't swing *this* way."

And, sure enough, when the flap

28

tried to flap back in, it couldn't. It hit the nail.

"So," he says to me. "You can go out. Feel free to go out. Feel free, in fact, not only to go out, but also to stay out, get lost, or disappear for ever. But should you bother to come back again, don't go to the trouble of bringing anything with you. Because this is now a one-way flap, and so you will have to sit on the doormat until one of the family lets you in."

He narrows his eyes at me, all nasty-like.

"And woe betide you, Tuffy, if there's anything dead lying waiting on the doormat beside you."

'Woe betide you'! What a stupid expression. What on earth does it mean anyway? 'Woe betide you'!

Woe betide *him*.

30

7: *Saturday*

I HATE SATURDAY morning. It's so unsettling, all that fussing and door-banging and "Have you got the purse?" and "Where's the shopping list?" and "Do we need catfood?" Of course we need catfood. What else am I supposed to eat all week? Air?

They were all pretty quiet today, though. Ellie was sitting at the table carving Thumper a rather nice gravestone out of half a leftover cork floor tile. It said:

Thumper
Rest in peace

"You mustn't take it round next-door yet," her father warned her. "Not till they've told us Thumper's dead, at any rate."

Some people are born soft. Her eyes brimmed with tears.

"There goes Next-door now," Ellie's
mother said, looking out of the
window.

"Which way is she headed?"

"Towards the shops."

"Good. If we keep well behind, we
can get Tuffy to the vet's without
bumping into her."

Tuffy? Vet's?

Ellie was even more horrified than I
was. She threw herself at her father,
beating him with her soft little fists.

"Dad! No! You can't!"

I put up a far better fight with my
claws. When he finally prised me out
of the dark of the cupboard under the
sink, his woolly was ruined and his
hands were scratched and bleeding all
over.

He wasn't very pleased about it.

"Come out of there, you great fat

furry psychopath. It's only a 'flu jab
you're booked in for – more's the
pity!''

Would *you* have believed him? I wasn't absolutely sure. (Neither was Ellie, so she tagged along.) I was still quite suspicious when we reached the vet's. That is *the only reason* why I spat at the girl behind the desk. There was no reason on earth to write HANDLE WITH CARE at the top of my case notes. Even the Thompson's rottweiler doesn't have HANDLE WITH CARE written on the top of his case notes. What's wrong with *me*?

So I was a little rude in the waiting room. So what? I *hate* waiting. And I especially hate waiting stuffed in a wire cat cage. It's cramped. It's hot. And it's boring. After a few hundred minutes of sitting there quietly, *anyone* would start teasing their neighbours. I didn't *mean* to frighten that little sick baby gerbil half to death. I was only

37

looking at it. It's a free country, isn't it? Can't a cat even *look* at a sweet little baby gerbil?

And if I was licking my lips (which I wasn't) that's only because I was thirsty. Honestly. I wasn't trying to pretend I was going to eat it.

The trouble with baby gerbils is they can't take a *joke*.

And neither can anyone else round here.

Ellie's father looked up from the pamphlet he was reading called "*Your Pet and Worms*". (Oh, nice. Very nice.)

"Turn the cage round the other way, Ellie," he said.

Ellie turned my cage round the other way.

Now I was looking at the Fisher's terrier. (And if there's any animal in the world who ought to have HANDLE WITH CARE written at the top of his case notes, it's the Fisher's terrier).

Okay, so I hissed at him. It was only a little hiss. You practically had to have bionic ears to *hear* it.

And I did growl a bit. But you'd think he'd have a head start on growling. He is a dog, after all. I'm only a cat.

And yes, okay, I spat a bit. But only a bit. Nothing you'd even *notice* unless you were waiting to pick on someone.

Well, how was *I* to know he wasn't feeling very well? Not *everyone* waiting for the vet is ill. *I* wasn't ill, was I? Actually, I've never been ill in my life. I don't even know what it *feels* like. But I reckon, even if I were *dying*, something furry locked in a cage could make an eensy-weensy noise at me

without my ending up whimpering and cowering, and scrabbling to get under the seat, to hide behind the knees of my owner.

More a *chicken* than a Scotch terrier, if you want my opinion.

"Could you please keep that vile cat of yours under control?" Mrs Fisher said nastily.

Ellie stuck up for me.

"He is in a cage!"

"He's still scaring half the animals in here to death. Can't you cover him up, or something?"

Ellie was going to keep arguing, I could tell. But, without even looking up from his worm pamphlet, her father just dropped his raincoat over my cage as if I were some mangy old *parrot* or something.

And everything went black.

No wonder by the time the vet came at me with her nasty long needle, I was in a bit of a mood. I didn't mean to scratch her that badly, though.

Or smash all those little glass bottles.

Or tip the expensive new cat scales off the bench.

Or spill all that cleaning fluid.

It wasn't me who ripped my record card into tiny pieces, though. That was the vet.

When we left, Ellie was in tears again. (Some people are born soft.) She hugged my cage tightly to her chest.

"Oh, Tuffy! Until we find a new vet who'll promise to look after you, you must be so careful not to get run over."

"Fat chance!" her father muttered.

I was just glowering at him through the cage wire, when he spotted Ellie's mother, standing knee-deep in shopping bags outside the supermarket.

"You're very late," she scolded. "Was there a bit of trouble at the vet's?"

Ellie burst into tears. I mean, talk about *wimp*. But her father is made of sterner stuff. He'd just taken the most huge breath, ready to snitch on me,

when suddenly he let it out again. Out
of the corner of his eye, he'd spotted
trouble of another sort.

"Quick!" he whispered. "Next-door
is just coming through the check-out."

He picked up half the shopping
bags. Ellie's mother picked up the rest.
But before we could get away,
next-door had come through the glass
doors.

So now all four of them were forced
to chat.

"Morning," said Ellie's father.

"Morning," said Next-door.

"Nice day," said Ellie's father.

"Lovely," agreed Next-door.

"Nicer than yesterday," said Ellie's
mother.

"Oh, yes," Next-door said.
"Yesterday was *horrible*."

She probably just meant the

weather, for heaven's sake. But Ellie's eyes filled with tears. (I don't know why she was so fond of Thumper. *I'm* the one who's supposed to be her pet, not *him*.) And because she couldn't see where she was going properly any more, she bumped into her mother, and half the tins of catfood fell out of one of the shopping bags, and rolled off down the street.

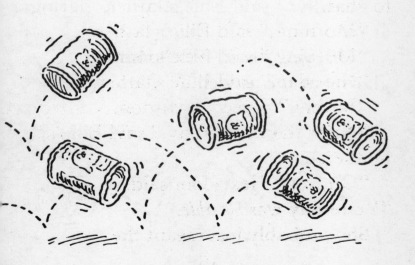

Ellie dumped down my cage, and chased off after them. Then she made the mistake of reading the labels.

"Oh, nooo!" she wailed. "Rabbit chunks!"

(Really, that child is such a *drip*. She'd never make it in our gang. She wouldn't last a *week*.)

"Talking about rabbit," said Next-door. "The most extraordinary thing happened at our house."

"Really?" said Ellie's father, glaring at me.

"Oh, yes?" said Ellie's mother, glaring at me as well.

"Yes," said Next-door. "On
Monday, poor Thumper looked a little
bit poorly, so we brought him inside.
And on Tuesday, he was worse. And
on Wednesday he died. He was
terribly old, and he'd had a happy life,
so we didn't feel too bad about it. In

fact we had a little funeral, and buried him in a box at the bottom of the garden."

I'm staring up at the clouds now.

"And on Thursday, he'd gone."

"Gone?"

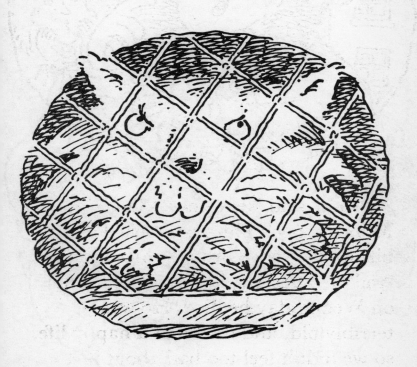

"Gone?"

"Yes, gone. And all there was left of him was a hole in the ground and an empty box."

"Really?"

"Good heavens!"

Ellie's father was giving me the most suspicious look.

"And then, yesterday," Next-door went on. "Something even more extraordinary happened. Thumper was back again. All fluffed up nicely, and back in his hutch."

"Back in his hutch, you say?"

"Fluffed up nicely? How strange!"

You have to hand it to them, they're good actors. They kept it up all the way home.

"What an amazing story!"

"How on earth could it have happened?"

"Quite astonishing!"

"So strange!"

Till we were safely through the front door. And then, of course, the pair of them turned on me.

"Deceitful creature!"

"Making us think you killed him!"

"Just pretending all along!"

"I *knew* that cat could never have done it. That rabbit was even fatter than he is!"

You'd have thought they all *wanted* me to have murdered old Thumper.

All except Ellie. She was *sweet*.

"Don't you *dare* pick on Tuffy!" she told them. "You leave him alone! I bet he didn't even dig poor Thumper up. I bet it was the Fisher's nasty, vicious terrier who did that. All Tuffy did was bring Thumper back to us so we could make sure he was buried again properly. He's a hero. A kind and thoughtful hero."

She gave me a big soft squeeze.

"Isn't that right, Tuffy?"

I'm saying nothing, am I? I'm a cat.
So I just sat and watched while they
unnailed the cat-flap.

Choosing a brilliant book
can be a tricky business...
but not any more

www.puffin.co.uk

The best selection of books at your fingertips

So get clicking!

Searching the site is easy – you'll find
what you're looking for at the click of a mouse,
from great authors to brilliant books and more!

Read more in Puffin

For complete information about books available from Puffin – and Penguin – and how to
order them, contact us at the appropriate address below. Please note that for copyright
reasons the selection of books varies from country to country.

www.puffin.co.uk

In the United Kingdom: Please write to Dept EP, Penguin Books Ltd,
Bath Road, Harmondsworth, West Drayton, Middlesex UB7 ODA

In the United States: Please write to Penguin Putnam Inc., P.O. Box 12289,
Dept B, Newark, New Jersey 07101–5289 or call 1–800–788–6262

In Canada: Please write to Penguin Books Canada Ltd,
10 Alcorn Avenue, Suite 300, Toronto, Ontario M4V 3B2

In Australia: Please write to Penguin Books Australia Ltd,
P.O. Box 257, Ringwood, Victoria 3134

In New Zealand: Please write to Penguin Books (NZ) Ltd,
Private Bag 102902, North Shore Mail Centre, Auckland 10

In India: Please write to Penguin Books India Pvt Ltd,
11 Panscheel Shopping Centre, Panscheel Park, New Delhi 110 017

In the Netherlands: Please write to Penguin Books Netherlands bv,
Postbus 3507, NL–1001 AH Amsterdam

In Germany: Please write to Penguin Books Deutschland GmbH,
Metzlerstrasse 26, 60594 Frankfurt am Main

In Spain: Please write to Penguin Books S. A., Bravo Murillo 19,
1° B, 28015 Madrid

In Italy: Please write to Penguin Italia s.r.l.,
Via Felice Casati 20, I–20124 Milano

In France: Please write to Penguin France S. A.,
17 rue Lejeune, F–31000 Toulouse

In Japan: Please write to Penguin Books Japan, Ishikiribashi Building,
2–5–4, Suido, Bunkyo-ku, Tokyo 112

In South Africa: Please write to Longman Penguin Southern Africa (Pty) Ltd,
Private Bag X08, Bertsham 2013

Y0-BTC-046

Common DOS Shell Operations

➤ indicates Menu selection sequence
→ indicates Program List selection sequence

■ Operation	■ Selection Sequence	■ Step
Associate files	File ➤ Associate	5
Attribute (change)	File ➤ Change Attributes	9
Back up hard disk	Disk Utilities → Backup Fixed Disk	7
Color (create)	Editor → C:\DOS\DOSSHELL.INI	11
Color (select)	Options ➤ Colors	2
Command prompt	F3 or Shift+F9	12
Confirm	Options ➤ Confirmation	8
Copy disks	Disk Utilities → Disk Copy	6
Copy files	File ➤ Copy	9
Delete directory	File ➤ Delete	7
Delete file	File ➤ Delete	9
Directory (create)	File ➤ Create Directory	7
Directory (select)	*directory icon*	7
Display mode (select)	Options ➤ Display	11
Drive (select)	*drive icon*	4, 12
Edit file	Main → Editor	15
Exit shell	F3 or File ➤ Exit	12
Files names (display)	Options ➤ File Display Options	4
Format disk	Disk Utilities → Quick Format	6
Help (shell)	F1 or Help	3
Hide file	File ➤ Change Attributes	9
Move file	File ➤ Move	9
Password protect	File ➤ Properties	10
Prevent program switch	File ➤ Properties ➤ Advanced	10
Print file	File ➤ Print	13
Program List (add)	File ➤ New	10
Program List (change)	File ➤ Properties	10
Protect file	File ➤ Change Attributes	9
Refresh screen	View ➤ Refresh	11
Rename file	File ➤ Rename	9
Rename directory	File ➤ Rename	7
Repaint screen	View ➤ Repaint Screen	12
Search for file	File ➤ Search	8
Select all files	File ➤ Select All	8
Select across directories	Options ➤ Select Across Directories	8
Show file information	Options ➤ Show Information	9
Task Swapper	Options ➤ Enable Task Swapper	5
Undelete file	Disk Utilities → Undelete	19
View (select)	View ➤ (select view)	11

The Up & Running Series from SYBEX

■ ■ ■ ■ ■ ■ ■ ■ ■ ■

Other titles include Up & Running with:

- AutoSketch 3
- Carbon Copy Plus
- DOS 3.3
- DR DOS 5.0
- Flight Simulator
- Grammatik IV 2.0
- Harvard Graphics
- Lotus 1-2-3 Release 2.2
- Lotus 1-2-3 Release 2.3
- Lotus 1-2-3 Release 3.1
- Norton Utilities
- Norton Utilities 5
- Norton Utilities on the Mactintosh
- PageMaker 4 on the PC
- PageMaker on the Macintosh

- PC Tools Deluxe 6
- PC-Write
- PROCOMM PLUS
- Q & A
- Quattro Pro 3
- Quicken 4
- ToolBook for Windows
- Turbo Pascal 5.5
- Windows 3.0
- Windows 286/386
- Word for Windows
- WordPerfect 5.1
- WordPerfect Library/ Office PC
- XTreeGold 2
- Your Hard Disk

Computer users are not all alike.
Neither are SYBEX books.

We know our customers have a variety of needs. They've told us so. And because we've listened, we've developed several distinct types of books to meet the needs of each of our customers. What are you looking for in computer help?

If you're looking for the basics, try the **ABC's** series, or for a more visual approach, select **Teach Yourself.**

Mastering and **Understanding** titles offer you a step-by-step introduction, plus an in-depth examination of intermediate-level features, to use as you progress.

Our **Up & Running** series is designed for computer-literate consumers who want a no-nonsense overview of new programs. Just 20 basic lessons, and you're on your way.

SYBEX **Encyclopedias** provide a comprehensive reference and explanation of all of the commands, features and functions of the subject software.

Sometimes a subject requires a special treatment that our standard series don't provide. So you'll find we have titles like **Advanced Techniques, Handbooks, Tips & Tricks,** and others that are specifically tailored to satisfy a unique need.

You'll find SYBEX publishes a variety of books on every popular software package. Looking for computer help? Help Yourself to SYBEX.

For a complete catalog of our publications:

SYBEX Inc.
2021 Challenger Drive, Alameda, CA 94501
Tel: (415) 523-8233/(800) 227-2346 Telex: 336311
Fax: (415) 523-2373

Up & Running with
DOS® 5

■ ■ ■ ■ ■ ■ ■ ■ ■ ■ ■

Alan Simpson

SYBEX®

San Francisco ■ Paris ■ Düsseldorf ■ Soest

Acquisitions Editor: Dianne King
Series Editor: Joanne Cuthbertson
Editor: Carol Henry
Project Editor: Kathleen Lattinville
Technical Editor: Joe Liburt
Word Processors: Paul Erickson, Deborah Maizels, Lisa Mitchell
Series Designers: Ingrid Owen, Helen Bruno
Icon Designer: Helen Bruno
Screen Graphics: Cuong Le
Desktop Production Artist: Helen Bruno
Proofreader: Dina F. Quan
Indexer: Ted Laux
Cover Designer: Archer Design
Screen reproductions produced by XenoFont

XenoFont is a trademark of XenoSoft.

SYBEX is a registered trademark of SYBEX, Inc.

TRADEMARKS: SYBEX has attempted throughout this book to distinguish propri-
etary trademarks from descriptive terms by following the capitalization style used
by the manufacturer.

SYBEX is not affiliated with any manufacturer.

Every effort has been made to supply complete and accurate information. However, SYBEX assumes no responsibility for its use, nor for any infringement of the
intellectual property rights of third parties which would result from such use.

Library of Congress Card Number: 90-71672
ISBN: 0-89588-774-6

Manufactured in the United States of America
10 9 8 7 6 5 4

SYBEX Up & Running Books

■ ■ ■ ■ ■ ■ ■ ■ ■ ■

The Up & Running series of books from SYBEX has been developed for committed, eager PC users who would like to become familiar with a wide variety of programs and operations as quickly as possible. We assume that you are comfortable with your PC and that you know the basic functions of word processing, spreadsheets, and database management. With this background, Up & Running books will show you in 20 steps what particular products can do and how to use them.

Who this book is for

Up & Running books are designed to save you time and money. First, you can avoid purchase mistakes by previewing products before you buy them—exploring their features, strengths, and limitations. Second, once you decide to purchase a product, you can learn its basics quickly by following the 20 steps—even if you are a beginner.

What this book provides

The first step usually covers software installation in relation to hardware requirements. You'll learn whether the program can operate with your available hardware as well as various methods for starting the program. The second step often introduces the program's user interface. The remaining 18 steps demonstrate the program's basic functions, using examples and short descriptions.

Contents & structure

A clock shows the amount of time you can expect to spend at your computer for each step. Naturally, you'll need much less time if you only read through the step rather than complete it at your computer.

Special symbols and notes

You can also focus on particular points by scanning the short notes in the margins and locating the sections you are most interested in.

In addition, three symbols highlight particular sections of text:

The Action symbol highlights important steps that you will carry out.

The Tip symbol indicates a practical hint or special technique.

The Warning symbol alerts you to a potential problem and suggestions for avoiding it.

We have structured the Up & Running books so that the busy user spends little time studying documentation and is not burdened with unnecessary text. An Up & Running book cannot, of course, replace a lengthier book that contains advanced applications. However, you will get the information you need to put the program to practical use and to learn its basic functions in the shortest possible time.

We welcome your comments

SYBEX is very interested in your reactions to the Up & Running series. Your opinions and suggestions will help all of our readers, including yourself. Please send your comments to: SYBEX Editorial Department, 2021 Challenger Drive, Alameda, CA 94501.

The goal of this book is to help experienced computer users get up to speed with DOS 5 quickly and easily. Here are some of the more important new features covered by *Up & Running with DOS ®5*:

- The new Shell provides a graphic interface to common DOS operations, including (finally) the ability to rename directories (Steps 2-11).

- You get on-screen help when you enter /? after a command (Step 12). Try **DIR /?** or **ERASE /?**.

- Many commands are improved; try **TREE **.

- DOSKey lets you record commands and create macros (Step 14).

- EDIT, a full screen editor, replaces Edlin (Step 15).

- You get improved control over memory and disk performance (Step 18).

- You can now successfully recover deleted files and accidentally reformatted disks directly from DOS (Step 19).

- You can have hard disk partitions greater than 32Mb—without loading SHARE (Step 20).

If you've already upgraded to version 5, this book will get you started using DOS 5's many new capabilities, in just 20 easy steps. If you haven't yet made the decision to upgrade, chances are you will after reading this book. It provides what the Up & Running Series offers to all busy computer users: the chance to learn what you need to know quickly, without having to wade through hundreds of pages of documentation.

Alan Simpson, May 1991

Table of Contents

Installation

▪ ▪ ▪ ▪ ▪ ▪ ▪ ▪ ▪ ▪ ▪

DOS (pronounced "dawss") is an acronym for *Disk Operating System*. On your computer, DOS plays the role of a high-level manager—it gives you (and the programs you use) a means of filing, locating, and retrieving information stored on your disks.

This book assumes you are already familiar with your computer, and have some familiarity with DOS (since the two are virtually inseparable). Nonetheless, let's take a moment to define some of the basic terminology that's essential to using DOS and your computer.

File: A disk *file* is the computer equivalent of a labeled manila file folder in a file cabinet. The disk file has a name up to eight characters long, followed by a period and a file name extension of up to three letters (for example, MYLETTER.TXT).

Basic DOS definitions

Directory: A *directory* is a collection of files, like a drawer in the file cabinet. To get to a file, you first need to know what directory (drawer) the file is in. Some programs automatically create their own directories, and you use DOS to create directories as well. Directory names are up to eight characters long.

Drive: Drive is short for *disk drive*. Files are stored magnetically on disk. The disk drives spin the disks so that the computer can store and read information on them. The drive can contain many directories, and each directory can contain many files. Floppy disk drives are named A and (if there are two) B; fixed (nonremovable) disk drives are named C, D, and so on. When used in commands, drive names are followed by a colon.

1

Path: This is any combination of drive, directory, and/or file names, separated by backslashes. For example, the *path name* C:\LETTERS\Jones.let tells DOS to take the path to drive C, then to the directory named LETTERS on that drive, and finally to the file named Jones.let on that directory.

Memory: Also called *main memory* or RAM, this is the place where the files with which you are currently working are stored. If the disk drives are like file cabinets that store all your information, then memory is your desktop, where the stuff you're using right now is stored. When the computer is turned off, memory is completely empty.

A large part of knowing how to use DOS (and your computer) effectively is learning how to locate files on the drives and directories, and to copy those files into memory so you can use them. DOS is the tool that allows you to do that.

This book is about the newest version of DOS, version 5. The first step to using DOS 5 is to install it on your computer. You need only install it once—not each time you want to use it. If you are not sure which version of DOS is stored on your computer, or whether DOS 5 needs to be installed, this chapter will help you to find out.

PREPARING FOR INSTALLATION

Before installing DOS 5, you should already know how to

- Turn on your computer
- Get (exit to) the DOS command prompt (typically A> or C>, followed by a blinking cursor) if another program or shell (such as Windows 3.0) appears when you first start your computer.

If you don't know these basics, refer to your computer's documentation, or ask someone who is familiar with your equipment. Then proceed to the next section.

Determining Your Current DOS Version

This book assumes that you are using DOS 5. If you are just getting started, or sitting at an unfamiliar computer, you may not know what version of DOS is currently installed. A simple way to find out is with the VER command, as follows:

1. Get to the DOS command prompt.

2. Type

   VER

   and press Enter.

You should see a message, such as "MS-DOS Version 5.00" (don't be concerned about the decimal portion of the version number, like .01 or .1). Then:

- If the VER command response shows that you are using version 5, skip to Step 2 of this book now.

- If you are using version 4 or earlier, continue reading here.

This Step will provide two separate sets of installation instructions—one set for hard (fixed) disks, and another set for computers with floppy drives only. Follow the instructions that match your hardware.

INSTALLING ON A HARD DISK

You can install DOS 5 on your hard disk without erasing anything or reformatting the disk. Just to play it safe, however, it's a good idea to back up the entire hard disk.

Hard disk installation

If you have a tape or other type of backup device, use it now to make your backup. Optionally, make sure that you have plenty of blank floppies handy, and proceed with the following instructions for DOS installation:

1. Fully insert the DOS 5 Setup Disk 1 in drive A or B on your computer.

2. Switch to that drive by typing its name, **A:** (or **B:**), and pressing Enter.

3. At the DOS prompt (A> or B>), type

    SETUP

    and press Enter.

4. As instructed on the screen, label one high-density floppy disk UNINSTALL #1, or label two low-density floppies UNINSTALL #1 and UNINSTALL #2. The disks should be either unformatted, or formatted but never previously used. These disks are for use only in drive A later, in case you decide to "uninstall" DOS 5.

5. Press Enter to proceed to the next screen.

6. If you are installing on a network, type **Yes** in answer to the next prompt, and follow the instructions on the screen. Otherwise, type **No** and proceed with the instructions here.

You will now decide whether or not to make a backup of your hard disk. If you have not already done so, you should select Backup the Hard Disks, and follow the instructions for performing the backup. (You'll also have an opportunity to terminate the installation if you do not have sufficient floppies to complete the backup.) If you have already backed up your entire hard disk, select Do Not Back Up the Hard Disks and proceed with the next step.

7. On the next screen, determine whether or not the installation program has correctly identified your computer. If so, press Enter to continue. Otherwise, make required changes as instructed on the screen.

8. On the next screen, type **Y** if you are ready to install, and follow the installation instructions that then appear.

When you have successfully installed DOS 5, you'll see instructions telling you to remove any floppies from disk drives and press Enter. Your computer will then automatically reboot, load DOS 5, and take you to the DOS 5 Shell (described in the next Step).

You should now store in a safe place the original disks that came with your DOS 5 package. You won't need them for normal daily computer use.

Starting DOS 5 on a Hard Disk

Now that DOS 5 is installed, you can start it up at any time as follows:

Startup on a hard disk

■   Make sure all floppy disk drives are empty.

■   Turn on the computer (and monitor if it has a separate switch).

DOS 5 will be loaded automatically.

INSTALLING ON FLOPPY DISKS

To install DOS 5 on a computer without a hard disk, or if you are just making an "installed" copy of DOS 5, first gather four blank 3½" floppies, or seven blank 5¼" floppies (as required by disk drive A). Then follow these steps:

Floppy disk installation

1.   Start your computer in the usual manner (typically by inserting the manufacturer's DOS Startup disk in drive A, and then turning on the computer).

2.   If it does not appear automatically, get to the DOS command prompt, usually A>. (For example, if the DOS 4 Shell appears, press F3 to exit to DOS.)

3.   Remove the disk currently in drive A, and insert the DOS 5 Disk 1.

4.   Type

   A:

   and press Enter to make sure you are on drive A.

5.   Type

   SETUP/F

   and press Enter to start the installation procedure.

6. Read the "Welcome to Setup" instructions that appear on your screen.

The screen now tells you how many blank disks you need, and how to label them. If you do not have a sufficient number of disks handy, press F3 to terminate the installation. You can resume later, after you've prepared your disks.

7. Label the blank disks as instructed on the screen, and then follow all remaining instructions that appear here and on successive screens.

8. When you have successfully completed the installation, you'll see a message indicating this, with a request to remove any floppy disks from the drive and place the newly created DOS 5 STARTUP disk in drive A. Do so, and then press Enter to start DOS 5.

You won't need the original DOS 5 disks for normal day-to-day operations. Instead, use the disks you made during installation. Store the originals in a safe place in case you lose or damage your new copies and need to repeat the installation procedure in the future.

Starting DOS 5 with Floppies

Startup with floppies

From now on, when you want to start your computer and DOS 5,

■ Insert the DOS 5 Startup Disk in drive A.

■ Turn on the computer (and monitor if it has a separate switch).

This will take you to the DOS 5 command prompt. In Step 2, you'll learn how to access the DOS 5 Shell from this point.

Using the DOS 5 Shell

The DOS 5 Shell offers a graphic means of interacting with your computer via DOS. Rather than displaying a passive, unhelpful command prompt, like some earlier versions of DOS, the Shell offers descriptive information and options for you to use immediately. Step 2 teaches you the basics of using the DOS 5 Shell.

ACCESSING THE SHELL WITH A HARD DISK

Depending on how you've installed DOS 5 on your hard disk, the Shell may appear automatically when you start your computer. If the command prompt (A> or C>) appears instead, you can quickly get to the Shell by following these simple steps:

Hard disk use of Shell

1. Type **DOSSHELL.**

2. Press Enter.

ACCESSING THE SHELL WITH FLOPPIES

If you don't have a hard disk, you can access the Shell by following these steps:

Floppy disk use of Shell

1. Remove the DOS 5 Startup disk from drive A.

2. Fully insert the disk labeled Shell (or Shell/Help) in drive A.

3. Type **a:** and press Enter to switch to drive A.

4. Type **DOSSHELL** and press Enter.

AREAS OF THE SHELL

Figure 2.1 shows an example of the Shell when it first appears; your screen may show somewhat different information, but don't worry about that. The circled numbers in the figure refer to the descriptions in Table 2.1, and do not appear on any Shell screen. Take a moment now to identify these basic areas of the Shell.

Number	Area/Window	Contents
1	Title bar	Name of current screen
2	Menu bar	Currently available options

Table 2.1: Areas of the DOS 5 Shell

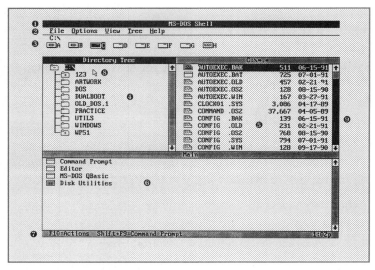

■ *Figure 2.1: Areas of the DOS 5 Shell*

Number	Area/Window	Contents
3	Disk drives	Current and available disk drives
4	Directory Tree window	Directories on the current disk drive
5	Files List window	Files on the current directory
6	Program List window	Available programs and program groups
7	Status line	Available keystrokes and current time
8	Mouse pointer	Where next mouse click will take effect
9	Scroll bar	Lets you access any information that does not fit in the window

Table 2.1: Areas of the DOS 5 Shell (continued)

In Step 11 of this book, you'll read about changing the arrangement and color scheme of the Shell screen.

Text vs. Graphics Screens

Figure 2.1 shows how the Shell appears on a graphics screen. If you do not have a graphics monitor, some of the icons will look different or will be missing altogether. However, all features of the Shell are still available to you.

Different or missing icons

Don't worry if your screen doesn't have exactly the same windows as in Figure 2.1. In Step 11 you'll learn how to select Program/File Lists from the View menu and change your screen to your liking. If the Active Task List window appears on your screen, you can hide it by selecting Enable Swapper from the Options menu (see Step 5).

Using a Mouse

One of the many advantages to using the Shell is that you can quickly access any part of the screen with a mouse or trackball. (In this book, we'll use the term "mouse" for both mice and trackballs.)

If you have a mouse, try rolling it (slowly) now to see its effect on the screen's mouse pointer.

Mouse terminology

When describing mouse use with the Shell, we'll use the following common terminology:

Click: Position the mouse pointer; then press and immediately release the *left* mouse button.

Double-Click: Position the mouse pointer; then click the *left* mouse button twice, quickly, without any time lag between the two clicks.

Drag: Position the mouse pointer; then hold down the *left* mouse button while rolling the mouse or trackball. Release the mouse button when finished dragging.

Left-handed mouse

If your mouse is installed for left-handed use, substitute "the *left* mouse button" with "the *right* mouse button" in each of the foregoing mouse action descriptions.

USING THE MENUS

The *menu bar* at the top of the Shell provides options for performing a variety of useful tasks. Each option on the menu bar is actually the name of a *pull-down menu* that appears after you select the option. Figure 2.2 shows you the pull-down menu for the File option.

On a pull-down menu, the options that you see are also called *commands*.

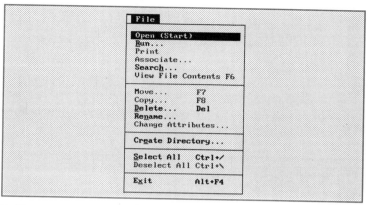

File

Open (Start)
Run...
Print
Associate...
Search...
View File Contents F6

Move...   F7
Copy...   F8
Delete...   Del
Rename...
Change Attributes...

Create Directory...

Select All   Ctrl+/
Deselect All Ctrl+\

Exit   Alt+F4

■ *Figure 2.2: The File pull-down menu*

Viewing a Pull-Down Menu

You can use either a mouse or the keyboard to access any pull-down menu.

To access a pull-down menu with a mouse, just click the name of the menu that you want to view.

Mouse

To access a pull-down menu with the keyboard,

Keyboard

1. Press and release the Alt key (or the F10 key). This activates the menu bar.

2. Use the ← and → keys to highlight the name of the menu you want to view, and then press Enter. Optionally, just type the underlined letter for that option.

The → , ← and other special keys on the numeric keypad work only when the Num Lock key is released.

Canceling a Pull-Down Menu

If you inadvertently access a pull-down menu, and want to cancel that action, here's how.

With a mouse, click any blank area outside the menu near the top of the screen, such as the title bar, or the blank space beyond the last menu option. *Or...*

On the keyboard, press the Esc key, or press Alt or F10 twice.

Once a pull-down menu is displayed, you can easily switch to other menus on the menu bar by pressing the ↑ and ↓ keys, or by clicking another option in the menu bar.

Understanding Menu Symbols

Commands on the pull-down menus follow certain conventions, as described in Table 2.2.

Shortcut keys

When DOS displays keystroke combinations, the + symbol means "hold down the first key, and then press the second one." Hence, Alt+F4 means "hold down the Alt key, press F4, and then release both keys." (Alt+F4 is a shortcut for exiting the Shell to the command prompt. To get back to the Shell, type **DOSSHELL** and Enter.)

Menu Symbol	Meaning
Ellipsis (...)	Selecting an option that's followed by an ellipsis takes you to a dialog box.
Dimmed appearance	This command does not apply to the current situation, and therefore is not available.
Diamond (♦)	For toggle (on/off) commands, this indicates that the option is currently on.
Key combination	A keystroke combination, such as Alt+F4 next to Exit on the File menu, is available as a shortcut to this command.

Table 2.2: Symbols Used in Pull-Down Menus

Selecting a Menu Option (Command)

Once you've displayed a pull-down menu, you can select any currently available command with either the mouse or keyboard.

To select a menu option with your mouse, just click the option you want.

Mouse

To select a menu option with the keyboard, *either*

Keyboard

Use the ↑ and ↓ keys to highlight the option you want, and press Enter. *Or...*

Type the underlined letter for that option.

USING DIALOG BOXES

Some commands on the pull-down menus will ask you for additional information via a *dialog box.* For example, selecting File Display Options from the Options menu brings you to the dialog box shown in Figure 2.3. Let's look at this example.

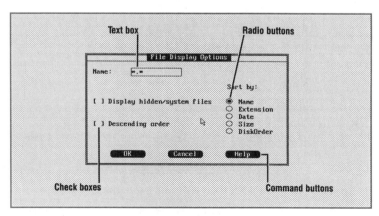

■ *Figure 2.3: A sample dialog box*

Moving within a Dialog Box

When a dialog box is displayed, you can move the cursor to various options and make selections. The current option contains the cursor, and may also be surrounded by a dotted line.

Mouse   To move to a different option in the dialog box using a mouse, click on the option or area you want to move to.

Keyboard   On a keyboard,

1. Press Tab to move down or to the right. Press Shift+Tab to move in the opposite direction.

2. Within a set of options (such as the radio buttons under Sort By: in Figure 2.3), use the four arrow keys to move the cursor in the direction you want to go.

Entering and Changing Text in Boxes

Some dialog boxes ask you to type into a text box within the dialog box, like the one next to the Name: option in Figure 2.3. To use a text box, first move the cursor into the box with either Tab or Shift+Tab, or by clicking the box with a mouse. (With a mouse, you can point to the exact point where you want to start typing.) Then,

■   To completely replace the contents of the box, just start typing your new text.

■   To change a part of the contents of the box, first move the cursor using the ← and → keys or your mouse, and then start typing.

■   To delete specific characters, position the cursor on the character you want to delete, and press the Del key.

■   To save the text, press Tab or Shift+Tab, or click another area with your mouse.

Filling Checkboxes

Many dialog boxes also have *checkboxes*. These let you control options that can be turned on by placing an *X* in the box, or turned off by leaving the box empty.

To use your mouse to activate (put an *X* into) a checkbox, or deactivate (remove the *X* from) a checkbox, click the checkbox.

Mouse

If you are using the keyboard,

Keyboard

1. Position the cursor in the box with Tab or Shift+Tab.
2. Press the spacebar.

Using Radio Buttons

Radio buttons in a dialog box are used to choose from a list of options. They work like the buttons used to select a station on a car radio—pressing a button automatically "unpresses" another button (you can't listen to two radio stations at once). The techniques for using radio buttons are similar to those for check boxes.

With a mouse, click the button option you want.

Mouse

On the keyboard,

Keyboard

1. Use Tab or Shift+Tab to move to the area of the radio buttons.
2. Use the ↑ and ↓ keys to move to the button you want.
3. Press Tab or Shift+Tab to move to another area.

It's not always easy to see the cursor in the radio buttons area. So watch the screen as you press Tab or Shift+Tab, and follow the cursor's movement.

Saving/Canceling Dialog Box Changes

Dialog boxes also contain a set of command buttons at the bottom that lets you save your choices and leave the box, or cancel the box without saving any entries, or get additional help if you need it. You use these buttons as you do the other buttons described above.

Mouse With a mouse,

- To save your entries and return to your previous location, click on OK.

- To leave the dialog box without saving any changes, click on Cancel.

Keyboard On a keyboard,

- To save your entries, press Enter; or navigate to the OK button using Tab or Shift+Tab, and press the spacebar or Enter.

- To leave the dialog box without saving any changes, press Esc; or move to the Cancel button using Tab or Shift+Tab, and press the spacebar or Enter.

 You'll read about the Help command button in the dialog box in Step 3 of this book.

CHOOSING ITEMS FROM A LIST

The main Shell screen, and many dialog boxes, present *scroll bars* to help you locate information in a long list. For example, Figure 2.4 shows an example of the Files window on the DOS Shell, with its scroll bar to the right.

A scroll bar functions when there are more available options than can fit within the window. The bar is a graphic representation of the overall list, as described here:

- The total length of the scroll bar (dark and light) represents the total length of the list.

- The white (or lighter) portion of the scroll bar, called the scroll box, shows what portion of the total list is currently displayed in the window.

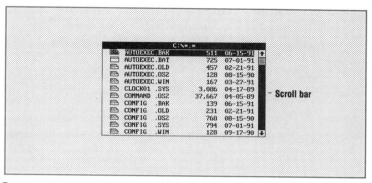

- *Figure 2.4: A scroll bar at the right of a window*

- The black (or darker) portion of the bar shows what portion of the list is currently not shown in the window.

You can use the scroll bar to scroll through a lengthy list to find the exact item you are looking for. Here's how.

Using a mouse,

Mouse

- To scroll up or down one line, click one of the scroll arrows at the top or bottom of the scroll bar.

- To scroll continuously, move the mouse pointer to one of the scroll arrows, and hold down the left mouse button.

- To scroll to a particular part of the list, drag the scroll box (the lighter portion of the scroll bar) to the approximate location that you want to view.

As an example of the last technique, suppose you are viewing an alphabetical listing of files, and want to view file names that begin with the letter *S*. Since *S* is about three-quarters of the way through the alphabet, move the mouse pointer to the scroll box, hold down the left mouse button, drag the scroll box about three-quarters of the way down the scroll bar, and then release the mouse button. You can then make additional adjustments by clicking the scroll arrows as necessary.

Keyboard

To use the scroll bars with the keyboard, first use Tab or Shift+Tab to move the cursor into the window with the scroll bar. Then,

- To scroll up or down a line, press the ↑ or ↓ key
- To scroll continuously, hold down the ↓ or ↑ key.
- To jump to the top of the list, press Home.
- To scroll to the end of the list, press End.

You will see examples of scroll bar use in future Steps.

AN ALTERNATIVE TO THE SHELL

In Step 12 of this book, you can read about the alternative method for interacting with DOS 5—through the command prompt.

Getting Help

DOS 5 offers many improvements over previous versions, by pro-
viding useful, accessible help on your screen. Learning to use the
built-in help system can be a great timesaver in finding new (or
forgotten) information without referring to written documentation.

GETTING IMMEDIATE HELP

The easiest way to get immediate, *context-sensitive help* (that is,
help with whatever you are doing at the moment) is to

*Immediate
help*

1. Select the option with which you need help, by clicking or
    moving the cursor to it.

2. Press F1.

If you are in a dialog box that has a Help command button, you
can get help in any one of these ways: Click the Help command
button; move the cursor to the Help command button and press
Enter (or the spacebar); or press F1.

Help appears on the screen in a *help window,* which offers the features summarized in Table 3.1.

Feature	Purpose
Help text	Provides help, with references to related topics in a different shade or color
Scroll bar	Lets you scroll to additional help text that does not fit within the window

Table 3.1: Help Window Features

Feature	Purpose
Close button	Returns you to the Shell
Back button	Takes you to the previous help screen, if any
Keys button	Provides help with keys and key combinations used with the Shell
Index button	Accesses the alphabetical help index (see Table 3.2)
Help button	Tells you how to use the help system

Table 3.1: Help Window Features (continued)

GETTING HELP ON RELATED TOPICS

You may see a related topic (colored) in the help text, with which you also need help. To see this additional information,

Mouse   With a mouse, double-click on the related topic.

Keyboard   Or, with the keyboard, press Tab until the related topic you want is highlighted, and press Enter.

A second help window, which partially overlaps the first, is displayed. You can get related help from this second window in the same way. To leave any help window and return to the previous one, select the Back button. To remove *all* the help windows, select the Close button or press Esc.

ACCESSING HELP FROM THE MENU

You can also gain access to the help system directly from the menu bar.

Mouse   To do so with a mouse, click on Help in the menu bar.

From the keyboard,

1. Press and release the Alt (or F10) key.

2. Type **H**, or highlight Help and press Enter.

The Help pull-down menu presents the options described in Table 3.2. Some of these are identical to Help window features (Table 3.1)—this is just an alternate route to them.

Menu Option	Result
Index	An alphabetical listing of help topics displayed in a window with a scroll bar. First select an alphabetical range of topics, and then the topic you want.
Keyboard	Keys and key combinations used with the Shell.
Shell Basics	A "minitutorial" on using the DOS 5 Shell, geared towards users who are already familiar with earlier versions of DOS.
Commands	Shell commands (menu options) organized by main menu topics. Another way to access context-sensitive help about specific commands.
Procedures	Step-by-step instructions for performing common tasks from within the Shell.
Using Help	Instructions on using the help system. A good way to learn the Shell's help system.
About Shell	Displays the current Shell version and copyright information.

Table 3.2: Options on the Help Pull-Down Menu (continued)

If you are just getting started with DOS 5, exploring the help system on your own now will be time well spent.

Navigating
Your System

One of the most important skills in using your computer effectively is the ability to find files when you need them. For example, you may need to "look around" to find a forgotten file. Or, when you are installing or running a program, you may need to first go to a particular drive and directory. Step 4 gives you the skills required to access specific drives, directories, and files.

SELECTING A DRIVE

To locate a particular file, you first need to get to the appropriate disk drive, or to select a disk drive to search for the file. To do this from the Shell, use the method best for you.

Click the drive's icon or name in the disk drives area of the Shell (just below the menu bar).

Mouse

Or, from the keyboard,

Keyboard

1. Press Tab until the highlighter is in the disk drives area.

2. Use the ← and → keys to highlight the drive you want, and then press Enter.

The name of the current drive remains highlighted in the disk drives area of the Shell, and also appears near the top of the Directory Tree and Files windows.

SELECTING A DIRECTORY

Every disk contains at least one directory, called the *root direc-tory,* named simply \. When you switch to a drive, the drive name and root directory name (and the icon) are automatically displayed at the top of the Directory Tree, followed by the names of any ad-ditional directories on that disk.

To switch to a different directory on the current disk drive, use ei-ther the mouse or the keyboard, as follows:

Mouse   Click the name of the directory you want.

Keyboard   Or, on the keyboard,

1.   Press Tab or Shift+Tab until the highlighter gets to the Di-rectory Tree window.

2.   Use the ↑ and ↓ keys to highlight the directory you want.

The Files window shows the names of files on the currently se-lected directory.

EXPANDING THE DIRECTORY TREE

You can organize your directories hierarchically. For example, Figure 4.1 shows a sample Directory Tree with three directories named 123, DBASE, and WP. The DBASE directory has three subdirectories beneath it, named LEDGER, PAYABLES, and RECEIVBL. These subdirectories contain files that are relevant only to the program on the DBASE directory.

In the Directory Tree, each directory beneath the root is consid-ered a *branch.* In Figure 4.1, for example, 123, DBASE, and WP are individual branches beneath the root. You can expand branches whose icons have a + sign in them, or collapse branches whose icons have a − sign in them, to view more or fewer levels of subdirectories.

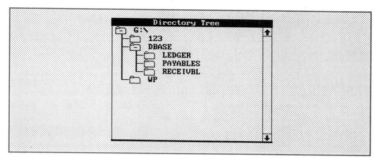

■ *Figure 4.1: A sample Directory Tree*

Expanding One Branch One Level

You can expand a single directory level and view the names of its subdirectories.

On a mouse, click the + sign of the directory icon.

Mouse

Or, if you're using a keyboard, highlight the name of the directory you want to expand. Then press the + key, or select Expand One Level from the Tree pull-down menu.

Keyboard

Fully Expanding One Branch

Even subdirectories can have subdirectories. Whenever you see a + in any directory icon, that directory has additional subdirectories that can be displayed. Rather than expanding the directory branch one level at a time, you can fully expand it by following these steps:

1. Select the directory that you want to fully expand.

2. Press the asterisk (*) key, or select Expand Branch from the Tree menu.

Fully Expanding All Branches

To see all the branches of the directory fully expanded, use either of these techniques:

- Press Ctrl+*. (To type the *, you can press either Shift+8, or the * key on your numeric keypad, if you have one. As you'll see, the asterisk (*) is often used in DOS to stand for "all.")

- Select Expand All from the Tree menu

To get some practice with all the foregoing navigation techniques, try experimenting with the disks and directories on your particular computer. Table 4.1 lists some additional shortcut keys that you can use to move through the Directory Tree and select the directories you need.

COLLAPSING DIRECTORY LEVELS

A minus sign (−) in a directory's icon means the branch can be collapsed. When you need to unclutter the Directory Tree window, here's how to collapse a branch.

Key	Selects This Directory
Home	Root directory (\)
End	Directory at the bottom of the tree
↑	Previous directory (if any)
↓	Next directory (if any)
First letter of directory name	First directory name on this level that begins with this letter

Table 4.1: Shortcut Keys for Navigating the Directory Tree

Mouse   Click the icon minus sign for the directory you want to collapse.

Keyboard   On a keyboard, highlight the branch you want to collapse. Then press the minus key, or select Collapse Branch from the Tree menu.

If the current active directory tree does not fit within the Directory Tree window, you can also use the scroll bar at the right of the window to scroll up and down the tree.

DISPLAYING FILE NAMES

Next to the Directory Tree window, the Files window displays the names of the files on the currently selected drive and directory (or subdirectory). It also shows the size of each file, and the date the file was created or last changed.

Viewing Selected File Names

When displaying file names, you can use two *wildcard* characters to isolate certain file names.

- A ? matches any single character in a file name

- An * matches any group of characters in a file name

Initially, DOS uses *.* (which you can see at the top of the Files window). This matches any file name followed by any extension—that is, every file name on the directory.

To limit the file selection to a particular file name pattern,

1. Be sure to first select the drive and directory that hold the files you want to view.

2. Select File Display Options from the Options menu.

3. Type in the file name, or pattern with wildcard characters.

4. Press Enter (or Esc to change your entry).

The Files window only displays file names that match the pattern you entered. With experience, you'll find this technique is particularly helpful when you have used a consistent pattern in naming your files. For example, if you store weekly data in separate files, and name those files WEEK1.DAT, WEEK2.DAT, and so forth, you can easily isolate those file names with the pattern WEEK*.DAT. This in turn makes it easier to move, copy, or delete these files as a group in the future, if necessary.

The file name or pattern you specify for the Files list carries over to other drives and directories. Thus, if you switch to a drive or directory that does not contain any files matching your specifier, the Files list shows the message "No files match file specifier."

Changing the Sort Order

The file names in the Files window are initially presented in alphabetical order by the first letter of the file name. There may be times, however, when another order is handy. For example, if you can't remember what name you gave to a file, but do remember the approximate date of creation, you might want to sort file names in date order, to isolate those created on a certain day.

To change the sort order of the Files display,

1. Select a drive and directory.

2. Select File Display Options from the Options menu.

3. Under Sort by:, select the radio button for one of these sort orders:

   Name: Alphabetical by file name (the default)

   Extension: Alphabetical by extension

   Date: Chronological by the date created or last changed

   Size: Smallest to largest size

   DiskOrder: Order in which file was placed on disk

4. Press Enter or click on OK.

Reversing the Current Sort Order

You may prefer to display file names in descending, rather than ascending order. To do so,

1. Select a drive and directory.

2. Select File Display Options from the Options menu.

3. Place an *X* in the Descending Order checkbox, and press Enter or click on OK.

Displaying Hidden/System Files

The Files window normally does not display hidden or system files (see Step 9). You can bring these file names out of hiding, if needed.

1. Select a drive and directory.

2. Select File Display Options from the Options pull-down menu.

3. Place an *X* in the Display Hidden/System Files checkbox, and press Enter or click on OK.

If there are no hidden or system files on the current directory, you won't notice any change.

The basic system navigation techniques outlined here make it easier for you to run programs and manage files, as described in the Steps that follow.

Running Programs

To run programs like word processors and spreadsheets is one of the main reasons most people buy computers. DOS 5 provides several alternative techniques for running programs, and the one you choose is pretty much up to your own personal preference.

ABOUT PROGRAMS

All programs are stored in *program files* (also called *executable* files) stored on disk. The name of a program file always has one of the following extensions: .EXE, .COM, or .BAT. The program's file name is also the command you use to start the program. For example, WP is the command to run a program named WP.EXE, or WP.COM, or WP.BAT.

STARTING A PROGRAM
FROM THE FILES WINDOW

The most straightforward way to start a program is to select its file name from the Files window of the Shell. To do so, you need to know the exact location and name of the program file. You can then use either the mouse or the keyboard to make the following selections:

- In the disk drives area, select the drive on which the program is stored.

- In the Directory Tree, select the directory that holds the program file. That is the program's *home directory.*

■ In the Files window, double-click the program's file name, or highlight its name and press Enter. (Remember: the file name must have the extension .EXE, .COM, or .BAT.)

When you exit the program, you'll be returned to the Shell.

STARTING A PROGRAM WITH THE RUN COMMAND

An alternative method for starting a program is by invoking the Run command on the File menu. Here are the steps to follow, using either a mouse or the keyboard at the Shell.

1. Select Run from the File menu.

2. In the dialog box, type the command line and any parameters that the program needs, as described in that program's documentation.

3. Click on OK, or press Enter.

If the requested program is not accessible from the current directory, you'll receive the "Bad command or file name" message.

When you run a program, keep in mind that whatever directory was current when you selected the Run command might remain current even after the requested program is running. Therefore, any files you create and save while using that program may be stored on the current directory, rather than the program's directory. To be sure you know how a particular program uses directories, refer to its documentation.

HOW DOS LOCATES A PROGRAM

Avoiding "Bad command or file name"

The "Bad command or file name" error message occurs when you try to run a nonexistent program, misspell a program name (or command), or try to run a program that is not accessible from the current directory. This last error is perhaps the most common, and the most confusing for many DOS users.

If you want to run a program without first changing to its home directory, you may need to include that location in the command line. For example, suppose you want to run your word processing program, which you normally start with the command WP. Let's say the program's home directory is C:\WP51. To run WP from a directory other than C:\WP51, you may need to type **C:\WP51\WP**, so that DOS can find the WP program files.

Notice that we say "may" in the above advice—because it all depends on how your computer is configured (a topic discussed in Step 17). Let's examine how DOS goes about responding to a command, such as your request to run the WP program.

- First DOS checks to see if the command is for one of its own internal programs (see Step 12).

- If the command is not an internal DOS command, DOS searches the current directory for the program file that has the .EXE, .COM, or .BAT extension.

- If DOS can't find the program on the current directory, it searches the directories specified in the current PATH setting.

- If DOS still cannot find the program, then it displays "Bad command or file name."

The most common technique for ensuring that a frequently used program is always accessible from any directory is to include its home directory in the current PATH setting (see Step 17).

ASSOCIATING FILES WITH PROGRAMS

Yet a third method of running programs from within DOS 5 is to set up an *association* between the program and the files that you create and change with that program.

For example, if you consistently use the file name extension .DOC to identify files created with a certain word processing program, you can associate that extension with that word processing program. From then on, whenever you double-click any .DOC file name, DOS will automatically load the associated word processing program, with the .DOC file you selected. (Keyboard users can highlight the file's name in the Files window, and then select Open from the Files menu, to load the file and its associated program.) Quite convenient!

Here's how to set up an association between a file name extension and a program.

1. Go to any directory that has at least one file of the type you want to associate with a program.

2. In the Files window, select a file name with the appropriate extension, either by clicking it once, or by highlighting it using the arrow keys.

3. Select Associate from the File menu.

4. If the program's home directory is not in the current PATH, type the complete path and the program command, as in **C:\WP51\WP**. If the program's home directory is in the PATH, you can just type the program's command or file name, like **WP.EXE** or **WP**.

5. Click on OK or press Enter to leave the dialog box.

To test the results, double-click any file that has the associated file name extension (or highlight it and press Enter). If the program does not load and run as you expect, keep in mind the following, and make corrections as necessary:

- The file name extension you associate with a program must be one that the program is capable of auto-loading. You'll have to refer to that program's documentation for details.

- You can associate up to 20 extensions with one program. For example, you might associate extensions like .DOC, .LET, and .TXT with your favorite word processing program. You cannot, however, associate an extension with more than one program. For example, you cannot associate the .DOC extension with a word processor and another text editor.

■ When the associated files are likely to be stored on several directories, it's best to have the program's home directory listed in the current PATH setting.

Temporarily Bypassing an Association

Suppose you set up an association between .DOC files and your word processor, but then later you want to use a different program (perhaps a spell-check program) to work with one of those files. In this case, you need not bother to dissociate the .DOC file and the word processor. Instead, just run the spell-check program on its own, perhaps by using the Run command on the File menu. Once that program is running, use its file retrieve or file import commands to pull in a copy of the .DOC file.

Terminating an Association

To "disconnect" a program and a file name extension, follow these steps:

1. Select any file name in the Files window that has the extension you want to dissociate.

2. Select Associate from the File menu.

3. Press Backspace to erase the association.

4. Click on OK, or press Enter.

RUNNING PROGRAMS FROM THE PROGRAM LIST

There is still another means of running a program from within DOS 5: the Program List window near the bottom of the screen.

In DOS's off-the-shelf configuration, the Program List contains only a handful of program options in the Main program group, and a few options in a group called Disk Utilities. Your own Program List might include other programs you may recognize. For example, if you share a computer with other users, you might see programs and program groups they have added. If the name of the program that you want to run is not displayed, it is probably part of one of the program groups listed.

Here's how to run any of the programs on the Program List.

Mouse With a mouse, first double-click the name of the program group that contains the program you want (if necessary). Then double-click the name of the program you want to run.

Keyboard If you are using a keyboard, first get the highlighter into the Program List. Then, if necessary, highlight the name of the group that contains the program you want to run and press Enter to select that group. Finally, highlight the name of the program itself, and press Enter.

You'll learn more about customizing and using the Program List in Step 10.

RUNNING MULTIPLE PROGRAMS

Task Swapper DOS 5 includes a Task Swapper, allowing you to easily switch from one active program to another without spending time exiting and reloading programs.

Activating the Task Swapper

To run multiple programs, you must first activate the Task Swapper.

■ Select Enable Swapper from the Options menu.

A new window, labeled Active Task List, is now added to the lower-right corner of the Shell screen. Also, notice that the Enable Task Swapper option now has a diamond next to it, indicating that the option is now active and available.

ADDING A PROGRAM TO A TASK LIST

To add a program to the Active Task List,

1. Make sure the Enable Swapper option is active.

2. Use any of the techniques described in this Step to run the program of your choosing.

3. To return to the Shell, press Alt+Tab.

Notice that the name of the program you've chosen now appears in the Active Task List. Repeat steps 1 and 2 to run as many programs as you wish.

Switching among Tasks

Once you have one or more tasks going in the Active Task List, you can easily move about among them.

Just double-click the name of the program to which you want to switch.   *Mouse*

Or, if you're using the keyboard, use the ↑ and ↓ keys to highlight   *Keyboard*
the name of the desired program. Then press Enter.

As a shortcut, you can switch back to the program that you left most recently just by pressing Alt+Tab again. Or, you can hold down Alt, and press Tab repeatedly to cycle through current tasks, shown near the top of the screen. When you see the name of the task you want, release the Alt key.

Keep in mind that—unlike OS/2 (a multitasking operating system) and Windows 3 (a multitasking DOS shell)—DOS 5 does not *run* all the programs in the Active Task List simultaneously. The moment you press Alt+Tab to leave a program and return to the Shell, that program is suspended, and does not resume its activities until you return to it.

Terminating a Task Normally

To terminate a task, thereby removing it from the task list, just select from the Task Swapper the program that you want to terminate. Then end and exit that program in the usual way.

While tasks are running, the Exit option on the File menu is
shaded and unavailable. But you can still make a temporary exit to
the command prompt by pressing Shift+F9.

Before turning off your computer, you should terminate all programs in the Active Task List, to prevent potential data loss. If you
make a habit of always exiting the Shell with the Exit option on
the File menu before turning off the computer, you'll be less likely
to lose unsaved data in memory.

Recovering from Abnormal Program Failure

If, for some reason, a program in the Active Task List crashes, and
you cannot terminate it normally, you can remove it from the Active Task List as follows:

1. Go to the Active Task List in the Shell.

2. Highlight the name of the program you want to terminate.

3. Select Delete from the File menu, or press the Del key.

The screen will remind you that you should use this technique
only as a last resort to terminate a program. If this is your last resort, select OK. Because the stability of DOS is compromised by
this action, you should next try to terminate all other programs in
the Task List normally. Then leave the Shell by selecting Exit
from the File menu. Finally, reboot the system with Ctrl+Alt+Del,
to restart DOS from scratch and bring it back to normal.

LAUNCHING BY DRAGGING

Yet another means of starting a program is with the mouse: You
move the highlight bar to a data file for a program (e.g., a
WordPerfect document file), then drag that file to the program file

name in the Files List (e.g., to WP.EXE for WordPerfect), and release the mouse button.

If the data and program files are not on the same drive and directory, you'll need to use the Dual File Lists view (Chapter 11). If the program file is not visible in the Files List window, drag the icon to either arrow in the scroll bar to scroll through the Files List.

Managing Disks

■ ■ ■ ■ ■ ■ ■ ■ ■ ■ ■

Floppy disks come in two sizes: 5¼" and 3½". The 5¼" disks are available in several capacities, most commonly 360K and 1.2Mb. The 3½" disks are available in 720K and 1.4Mb capacities. The correct disk size and capacity for your particular computer is determined by the floppy drives installed.

SELECTING A FLOPPY DRIVE

To view the files on a floppy disk in the Files window,

1.   Place the floppy disk in drive A or drive B.

2.   Double-click or press Enter on the drive's icon in the disk drives area.

If you change the disk in drive A or B, repeat step 2 to update your Files list.

If you plan to leave the drive empty after removing a disk, first switch to one of the hard disks by clicking its drive (C, D, or a higher letter), and then remove the floppy from its drive.

ABOUT FORMATTING

When you buy a new box of blank disks, they might not yet be *formatted* for use on your computer (though it is possible to buy preformatted disks). Unformatted disks must be formatted before you can use them in your computer.

Any disk that already has useful information or programs on it should *never* be formatted. Formatting a disk completely erases all its stored information.

Also, avoid reformatting your hard disk, as doing so will erase all its files. (If you inadvertently reformat a formatted disk, you may be able to recover your files by "unformatting," as described in Step 19 of this book.)

Determining If a Disk is Formatted

Avoiding formatting mistakes

If you are not sure whether a disk is already formatted, you should find out *before* you format it. Just insert the disk in drive A or B, and select that drive letter from the disk drives area on the Shell.

If you see the message "General Failure," the disk is not yet formatted, so it's OK to format the disk (first press Esc to leave the error message window). If you don't see the message, the disk is already formatted, and you should not reformat it.

Formatting a Floppy Disk

To format a floppy disk, follow these steps:

1. Select your hard disk drive, or place your DOS Startup disk in drive A and select that drive.

2. Insert the unformatted disk in drive A, or B if you are using two floppy drives.

3. In the Program List near the bottom of the screen, select Disk Utilities from the Main program group. (You may need to first select the Main program group in order to get to Disk Utilities.)

4. Select Format.

5. If you are formatting the disk in drive B, type **b:** in the text box. Otherwise, leave the default **a:** as is.

6. Select OK (or press Enter).

7. When you see the

   `Insert new diskette...`

   message, press Enter to continue.

8. When formatting is complete, you'll see

   `Volume label (11 characters, ENTER for none)?`

You can add an "electronic" volume label up to 11 characters long, which will then appear on the screen whenever you look at the contents of the disk. Press Enter after typing the label. If you choose not to add a volume label, just press Enter. *Volume labels*

The screen then displays the total available disk space, some other information about the disk, and the option

`Format another (Y/N)?`

If you want to format another disk, type **Y** for Yes and follow the instructions on the screen. Otherwise, type **N** and press Enter.

QUICK FORMAT

Notice that the Disk Utilities group also contains a Quick Format option. This option is generally used to reformat formatted disks, thereby quickly erasing all the files from the disk. To use Quick Format, follow the same basic steps you use for Format, described above, except choose Quick Format rather than Format in step 4. Also, note that if you try to Quick Format a disk that has not been previously formatted, you'll see a message asking if it's OK to proceed with an unconditional (normal, slower) format. Type **Y** if you want to proceed.

Note than when Quick Format is done, the Files list for the reformatted disk still shows the old file names. To update the list, just double-click that drive's icon.

If you inadvertently Quick Format a disk and erase all of its files, you *may* be able to unformat the disk and recover your files (see Step 19).

Formatting for Lower-Density Drives

Floppy disk compatibility

If you have high-capacity (1.4Mb or 1.2Mb) drives, you can format disks in those drives for use in lower-capacity drives. This is handy when, for instance, you need to format a disk and copy files to it, and then use that disk in a computer that does not have high-capacity drives.

- To format a 360K disk in a 1.2Mb drive, use the /f:360 switch in the Format command.

- To format a 720K disk in a 1.4Mb drive, use the /f:720 switch.

For example, if your drive A is a 1.2Mb drive, and you want to format a disk for use in a 360K drive, enter

```
a: /f:360
```

in the Format dialog box (as described in the preceding section). If your drive B is a 1.44Mb floppy drive, and you want to format a disk for use in a 720K drive, enter the following in the dialog box:

```
b: /f:720
```

FORMATTING BOOTABLE DISKS

System tracks

Whenever you start your computer, it automatically searches for the *system tracks* on drive A (or on drive C if a hard disk exists). A disk that contains a copy of the system tracks is called a *bootable disk,* because the computer can "boot itself up" from that disk.

Even if you normally boot from a hard disk, it's a good idea to keep a bootable floppy around. That way, if the system tracks on your hard disk become corrupted, you can still get your computer started with your spare boot disk.

If you try to boot a computer from a non-bootable disk, you get the error message "Non-system disk or disk error" until you insert a bootable disk.

You can format a floppy disk and copy the system tracks to it at the same time, by using the optional /s switch with the Format command. For example, to format the disk in drive A as a bootable disk (in step 5 of the preceding formatting procedure), type

The /s switch

```
A: /s
```

in the text box.

To format the disk in drive A as a bootable 360K disk, you can combine the two switches, like this:

Combining switches

```
A: /f:360 /s
```

If you don't have a hard disk, place your DOS Startup disk in drive A, and a blank disk in drive B. Then use **B:** /s in your Format command.

No hard disk

The copied boot disk contains the hidden system files IO.SYS, MSDOS.SYS, and the COMMAND.COM file, which contains DOS's internal commands. The disk does *not* contain the CONFIG.SYS or AUTOEXEC.BAT files (used to configure your system), or any external DOS commands. See "Copying Essential Files to Boot Disk," later in this Step.

Leaving Room for System Tracks

Suppose you want to copy some files to a floppy, and give it to someone else to use. If that user has no hard disk, she may want to boot up with the disk you supplied. To make it bootable, that user will need to copy her version of DOS to that disk. (Because your own copy of DOS is protected by copyright laws, you're not allowed to give away copies of it.) You will therefore need to leave room on the formatted disk for the system tracks, so use the /b switch instead of the /s switch with the Format command.

Copying the System Tracks Only

If you've left room for the system tracks on a formatted disk, you can then use the SYS command to copy any version of DOS to that disk. Remember to also copy the DOS COMMAND.COM program to the disk, as well. For example, if you are copying from a hard disk,

1. In drive A, insert a disk formatted with the /b switch.

2. Select your hard disk drive C.

3. Select Run from the File menu.

4. Type

   SYS A:

   and press Enter (or select OK).

If you're using floppies, place your DOS Startup disk in drive A and choose that drive. Place the disk you formatted with the /b switch in drive B, and use the command **SYS B:** rather than SYS A: in step 4 above.

5. When SYS completes its job, you'll see the message "System transferred." Press any key to return to the Shell.

Adding Essential Files to Boot Disk

For the boot disk to be a functional startup disk, it must contain the COMMAND.COM file. To check for this file in the disk's current contents, click its icon (A or B) in the drives area of the Shell, and look at the Files window. If COMMAND.COM isn't there, copy it from the C:\DOS directory of your hard disk to the boot floppy (see Step 9 for how to copy files). You'll also need to create (or copy) CONFIG.SYS and/or AUTOEXEC.BAT files if you want the disk to perform configurations at bootup (see Step 17).

UNUSUAL FORMATS

If you need to format disks for use with an older disk drive, and you know the exact number of tracks, and sectors per track you need, you can use any combination of the optional switches shown in Table 6.1 to get the exact format you want.

Switch	Effect
/1 (one)	Formats a single side only
/4	Formats a 360K disk in a 1.2Mb drive (like /f:360)
/8	Formats eight, rather than nine sectors per track
/N:x	Formats the number of sectors per track specified by x
/T:x	Formats the number of tracks specified by x

Table 6.1: Switch Options for Formatting Floppies

COPYING DISKS

To make an exact copy of a disk (for example, as a backup to your original), follow these steps:

Copying entire disks

1. Place the disk you want to copy in drive A.

2. If you have two *identical* floppy drives, place a blank disk (it need not be preformatted) in drive B. (Do so *only* if the drives are identical—both 5¼" 1.2Mb, or both 3½" 720K.)

3. If you have not done so already, select Disk Utilities from the Main program group.

4. Select Disk Copy (by double-clicking, or highlighting and pressing Enter).

5. If you have two identical drives, press Enter or select OK to accept the suggested **a: b:** in the text box. If you have two different drives, change the drive letters to **a: a:**. Then press Enter or select OK.

6. Follow the instructions that appear on the screen. (Keep in mind that the *source* disk is the original disk that you are copying, and the *target* disk is the one that's receiving the copied files.)

To copy files across disks of two different sizes, or between a hard drive and a floppy drive, use the copying techniques in Step 9.

COMPARING DISKS

After copying a disk using the Disk Copy option (in the foregoing section), you can verify the copy, if you wish, using the Disk Compare (DISKCOMP) command. Here's how.

1. If you have two identical floppy drives (as described above) insert the two disks to be compared in the drives. For two different drives, place one of the disks to be compared in drive A.

2. Select Run from the File menu.

3. If you have two identical drives, type

   `DISKCOMP A: B:`

   Otherwise, if you're using only one drive, type

   `DISKCOMP A: A:`

4. Press Enter or select OK.

5. Follow any instructions that appear on the screen. You'll eventually see a message indicating whether the two disks are identical.

You can compare individual files across different disk types. The basic steps are the same as for comparing disks, except that, rather than using DISKCOMP, you use COMP or FC, followed by the location and names of the files you want to compare. Here are examples.

```
fc c:\123\budget.wk1 a:\123\budget.wk1
comp c:\123\budget.wk1 a:\123\budget.wk1
```

COMP is generally used to determine if two files are identical. If the files are not the same size, COMP tells you so. This, of course, means the files are not identical. FC compares files even if they're not the same size, and lists any differences it encounters.

Managing
Your Hard Disk

This Step shows you how to manage your hard disk through the efficient use of directories, as well as techniques for backing up the hard disk.

CREATING A DIRECTORY

Directory names, like file names, can be up to eight characters long, with an extension of up to three characters. It's customary, however, to omit the extension in directory names to avoid confusion with file names.

Directory names

To create a directory one level beneath the root directory,

1. Make sure to highlight, in the disk drives area, the drive on which you want this directory to reside.

2. Select the name of the root directory for that drive (for example, C:\) from the Directory Tree.

3. Select Create Directory from the File menu.

4. Type the directory name, and press Enter (or select OK).

Creating a Subdirectory

To create a subdirectory under an existing directory (other than the root), follow the same procedure described above for creating a new directory. Just be sure to first select the directory (or subdirectory) name that is one level above the new subdirectory you want to create.

For example, to create a subdirectory named WPFILES beneath an existing directory named WP51 (that is, a subdirectory called \WP51\WPFILES), first select the WP51 directory in the Directory Tree, so that its name is highlighted and its files appear in the Files window. *Then* select Create Directory from the File menu, enter the subdirectory name in the dialog box (WPFILES in this example), and press Enter or select OK.

Accessing a sub-directory

An added subdirectory name appears in the Directory Tree beneath its parent (higher-level) directory, but the parent directory remains the selected (active) directory. To switch to the new subdirectory, select it with your mouse or keyboard.

In most cases, when the word "directory" is used in this book, it also means "subdirectory."

RENAMING A DIRECTORY

To change the name of any directory or subdirectory,

1. Highlight the name of the directory you want to rename.

2. Select Rename from the File menu.

3. Type the new name, and press Enter (or select OK).

REMOVING A DIRECTORY

You can remove an existing directory from the tree *only if it does not contain files, and only if it has no subdirectories.*

To remove an empty directory or subdirectory,

1. Select the name of the directory you want to delete from the Directory Tree.

2. Select Delete from the File menu (or press Del).

3. In response to the confirmation inquiry, select Yes if you are sure you want to complete the delete action.

If you receive the message "Access denied," then the directory is not empty. Select Cancel; then erase or move any files on the directory (see Step 9 of this book), and/or remove any subdirectories beneath that directory.

BACKING UP A HARD DISK

Because there is always the outside chance that a hard disk will crash (which destroys all your files), it's a good idea to keep floppy disk backups of all your hard disk files. Initially, you'll need to back up the entire hard disk, which you may already have done during DOS 5 installation. The first backup will probably require a good number of floppies.

To determine how many floppies you'll need to back up a single hard disk drive, you first need to determine how many bytes are stored on that drive. To do so,

1. Make sure the correct drive (the one you are backing up) is selected in the Shell.

2. Select Show Information from the Options menu.

3. Using the numbers under the heading "Disk" near the bottom of the window, subtract the available amount of space from the total disk size.

    For example, if the Disk Size: entry is 33,323,000 bytes, and the Avail: entry is 10,000,000 bytes, then there are 23,323,000 bytes stored on the disk. Thus, if you are using 1.2Mb floppies, you'll need at least 23 floppies to back up that one hard drive.

    How many floppies?

4. To remove the Show Information window from the screen, press Enter or click OK.

Ready all your backup floppies by labeling and numbering them with adhesive labels. You might label them Drive C Backup 001, Drive C Backup 002, Drive C Backup 003, and so forth.

Labeling backup disks

Preparing Floppies for Multiple Hard Disks

If you have several hard drives (D, E, and so on) you'll need to repeat the foregoing procedure, and label additional floppies as required, for each additional drive that you want to back up.

Initial Backup

To back up a hard disk for the first time,

1. Make sure the correct drive and its root directory are selected in the Shell.

2. In the Program List, select Disk Utilities from the Main program group.

3. Select Backup Fixed Disk by double-clicking, or highlighting and pressing Enter.

4. The Backup Fixed Disk dialog box appears (Figure 7.1). If appropriate to your situation, you can accept these default parameters, as shown in the figure, and as defined here:

*Backup
switches
and options*

`c:\*.* a: /s`

c: inticates the root directory of drive C

. indicates all files

a: represents the drive that holds the disk that will receive the files backup

/s includes every file on all directories

Or, if you are *not* backing up hard disk drive C, change the **c:** parameter to the appropriate drive letter. If you are using floppies in drive B rather than A, change the **a:** parameter to **b:**.

5. After accepting or changing the backup parameters in the text box, press Enter or select OK to proceed with the backup.

6. Follow the screen instructions for replacing the disk in drive A or B.

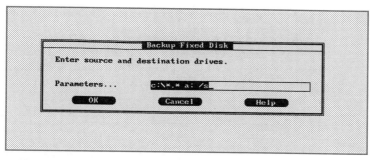

- *Figure 7.1: The Backup Fixed Disk dialog box*

When the backup is complete, you'll be returned to the Shell.

Backing Up Altered Files Only

After the initial backup, you can save a lot of time by backing up only files that are new or were modified since the last backup. It's not easy to determine how many additional floppies you'll need for this partial backup, so try to keep plenty of blanks on hand, and be sure to number them consecutively, as well. For example, if your last backup disk is labeled Drive C Backup 023, number additional backup disks starting at 024.

To perform the partial backup, repeat the same steps you followed to perform the initial backup, but in step 4 change the /s switch to /a. (The /a tells DOS to back up only those files that have been created or modified since the previous backup.) Then follow the instructions for completing the backup that appear on your screen.

Partial backups

RESTORING BACKUP FILES

Should your hard disk crash and need to be replaced or reformatted, here's how to restore all your files from backups to the new/repaired hard disk.

Recovering lost files

1. On the Shell, select the hard disk drive that you want to restore.

2. Insert in a floppy drive the backup disk numbered 001 for the drive being restored.

3. On the Program List, select the Disk Utilities group. Then choose Restore Fixed Disk by double-clicking, or highlighting it and pressing Enter.

4. Type

    `a: c:\ /s`

    where **a:** is the floppy drive, **c:** is the hard drive you're restoring, and \ is the root directory. Enter the drive letters appropriate to your situation.

5. Press Enter or select OK, and follow the directions that appear for completing the file restoration.

You'll need to repeat the restoration procedure for each hard disk in your computer. (See your original DOS 5 documentation for additional options and switches supported by BACKUP and RESTORE.)

Using
the Files Window

■ ■ ■ ■ ■ ■ ■ ■ ■ ■ ■

This Step introduces basic techniques for using the Files List window of the Shell, to prepare you for the file management actions (copying, moving, renaming, and deleting) covered in Step 9.

SELECTING A SINGLE FILE

Before you can work with a file, you must select its name from the Files window. When a file is selected, its icon is darkened (or, on a text screen, a ▶ symbol appears next to the file name).

To select a file with a mouse, click the file name.

Mouse

From the keyboard, press Tab or Shift+Tab until you reach the Files List window. Then use any combination of the Home, End, PgUp, and PgDn keys, the first letter of the file name, and the ↑ and ↓ keys to highlight the name of the file you want.

Keyboard

The selected file will remain selected, even when you move to another Shell area or activate a menu.

SELECTING MULTIPLE FILES

You can also select groups of files; they may be adjacent or scattered in the Files list.

To select multiple file names with a mouse,

1. Click the Files List window and locate the name of the first file that you want to select (using the scroll bar and/or the first letter of the file name).

2. Click the file name.

3. To select additional adjacent file names, hold down the Shift key and click the last name in the group of files that you want.

4. To select yet more files or groups, hold down the Ctrl key and click the name of the file you want.

5. If you want to select additional adjacent file names starting at the file you just selected, hold down Ctrl+Shift and click the last name in the group of files you want. (You can still use the scroll bar, even while holding down the Ctrl key.)

6. Repeat steps 4 and 5 as necessary to select all your file names.

To "deselect" a selected file name, hold down Ctrl and click the file name again. *Caution:* Keep in mind that if you click the mouse *without* holding down the Ctrl or Shift+Ctrl keys, this will immediately deselect all your current selections, so keep your finger on that Ctrl key!

Keyboard   To select multiple files using the keyboard,

1. Press Tab or Shift+Tab as needed, to get to the Files List window.

2. Press Add (Shift+F8); the word ADD appears in the status line.

3. Highlight the first file that you want to select, and press the spacebar to select it.

4. To select additional adjacent file names, hold down the Shift key and use ↑ and ↓ to scroll through the files that you want to select. Then release the Shift key.

5. Move the highlight bar to the next file that you want, and press the spacebar to select it.

6. Repeat steps 5 and 6 as necessary to select all the files you want.

To deselect a selected file name, highlight it and press the spacebar.

To select a group of files with similar dates or extensions, first use the File Display Options on the Options menu to change the sort order to Date or Extension. When you come back to the Files window, all the files with identical dates or extensions will be grouped.

SELECTING FROM MULTIPLE DIRECTORIES

You can also select files from multiple directories.

1. Choose Select Across Directories from the Options menu.

2. Using any method described in the preceding paragraphs, select files from any directory. Then switch to another directory and select files there. You can select files from as many directories as you wish.

For additional ways of selecting files from multiple directories, see "Searching for Files" later in this Step, and the Dual Files List view option in Step 11.

SELECTING ALL FILES

To select all the files currently displayed in the Files window,

■ Choose Select All from the Files menu, or press Ctrl+/.

You can use the File Display options on the Options menu to display a particular pattern of file names, such as *.BAT, and then use Select All on the Files menu to quickly select all those files.

DESELECTING FILES

Here's how to deselect ("unselect") a selected file.

With a mouse, hold down the Ctrl key and simply click the name of the file you want to deselect.

Or, on a keyboard,

1. If ADD is not displayed in the status line, press Shift+F8.

2. Use the ↑ and ↓ keys to highlight any selected file name, and press the spacebar to deselect it.

If you want to deselect *all* the currently selected file names,

■ Choose the Deselect All option from the File menu, or press Ctrl+\ .

SEARCHING FOR FILES

If you can't remember which directory holds a particular file, or if you want to gain access to a certain type of file across directories (such as all .BAK files), follow these steps:

1. Select the drive you want to search.

2. Select Search... from the File menu.

3. Enter the name of the file you want to find, or a file name pattern (such as *.BAK or MAR??.DOC).

Search-ing all directories

4. To search all directories, place an *X* in the Search Entire Disk checkbox. Clear it if you want to search the current directory only.

5. Press Enter or select OK.

A list of files, each one with its path, overlays most of the Shell screen. From here you can select individual files or groups of files, just as you can within the Files window of the Shell. The menu bar is left active at the top of the screen, so that you can also perform basic file operations, such as moving, copying, and deleting (see Step 9) on the located files.

To return to the basic Shell screen,

■ Press Esc, or select Program/File Lists from the View pull-down menu.

Managing Files

This Step is a lesson on basic techniques for managing individual and groups of selected files.

CONTROLLING CONFIRMATION BOXES

As a safety net, DOS 5 offers *confirmation boxes* when you delete, move, or copy files. There are three types of confirmation.

Confirm on Delete   Asks for permission before deleting files.

Confirm on Replace   Displays the name, size, and date of any file that's about to be replaced, along with the file that's about to replace it, and asks for permission to replace.

Confirm on Mouse Operation   Asks for permission before completing a copy or move action that you perform with a mouse.

The following *confirmation responses* are (generally) available:

Yes   Proceed with the replacement/deletion.

No   Do not replace/delete this file, but proceed with other selected files (if any).

Cancel   Do not delete/replace this file, and do not continue with other selected files.

Confirmation boxes appear only if activated. To activate or deactivate confirmation boxes,

1. Select Confirmation from the Options menu.

2. Click or press the spacebar to activate (put an *X* in) or deactivate (clear) any confirmation options.

3. Press Enter or select OK.

COPYING FILES

Once you have selected a file name or group of file names in the Files List, you can then copy those files. To do so,

1. Select Copy from the File menu (or press F8).

2. In the To: portion of the dialog box, enter the complete path to which you want the files copied.

3. Press Enter or click OK.

The path you enter in step 2 of the preceding instructions must be an existing directory, and must be in proper DOS syntax. For example, **A:** for the root directory of the disk in drive A, or **C:\WP51\OLDSTUFF** for the OLDSTUFF subdirectory under the WP51 directory.

If any files will be replaced during the copy operation, and you've activated "Confirm on Replace," you'll be asked for confirmation of your command before DOS replaces any files.

Names of nonexistent directories are treated as file names. For example, if you copy a file to C:\NOSUCH, and DOS cannot find a directory named NOSUCH, the copy will be sent to a file named NOSUCH in the root directory of drive C—*without* any warning or error message.

Copying to the Same Directory

It's easy to copy a file to a different file name on the same directory—for instance, you might want to make a copy of MYLETTER.WP, named MYLETTER.BAK.

1. In the Files List, choose the file you want to copy. (You can select only one file name in this operation.)

2. Select Copy from the File menu.

3. Press →.

4. If a backslash (\) does not already appear at the cursor position, type a backslash.

5. Type the name of the file to which you want to copy the selected files.

6. Press Enter or select OK.

Copying by Dragging a Mouse

If you have a mouse, you can quickly copy any file to any directory on the same drive, by dragging the file name to the directory. If you drag the file icon to a disk drive icon, the file is copied to the root directory of that drive.

1. Point to the name of the file you want to copy.

2. Hold down the mouse button, and drag the file icon to the icon of the directory to which you are copying the file.

3. Release the mouse button.

If the "Confirm on Mouse Operation" option is on, you'll be asked for permission to complete the copy. For information on dragging files across drives, see "Using the Dual File List View" in Step 11.

*Confir-
mation*

While you are dragging an icon to a different area of the Shell, the icon turns into an international "No" symbol whenever you're in a Shell area to which that icon cannot be copied.

MOVING FILES

After selecting files from the Files area, follow these steps to move them:

1. Select Move from the File menu (or press F7).

2. In the To: portion of the dialog box that appears, enter the complete path of the directory to which you want to move the files; for example, A:\ or C:\WP\EXTRA.

3. Press Enter or click OK.

Moving by Dragging a Mouse

If you have a mouse, you can drag a single file from one directory to another directory. To move a file by dragging, just use the same procedure listed previously for copying by dragging.

*Confir-
mation*

As with copying, if the "Confirm on Mouse Operation" option is on, you'll be asked for permission to complete the move.

See Step 11 for tips on using the Dual File Lists view to drag files across drives.

RENAMING FILES

To change the name of a selected file or group of files, select Rename from the File menu. Then enter the new file name in the New Name: text box as prompted. If you selected several files when you chose Rename, you'll be prompted to enter a new name for each selected file.

When renaming a file, you cannot enter a different drive or directory name in an attempt to also move the file. You must use the Move options, described earlier, instead.

DELETING FILES

After you've selected a file or group of files for deletion from your disk, follow these steps:

1. Select Delete from the File menu (or press Del).

*Confir-
mation*

2. If "Confirm on Delete" is active, you'll be asked to confirm your command before DOS deletes the files. Select OK to process the deletion.

If you accidentally delete files, you may be able to recover them.
See Step 19 for more information.

FILE ATTRIBUTES

You can assign any of the following attributes to a file:

Hidden   File name does not appear in the Files List (unless
Display Hidden/System Files is activated in the File Display
Options of the Options menu). You can turn this attribute on to
hide a file name.

System   This is an MS-DOS system file.

Archive   File has been modified since the last Backup operation. DOS assigns this attribute automatically, so that the file
will be backed up when the Backup /a command is next used.

Read-Only   File contents can be viewed but not modified;
there is an extra warning when a delete command is issued. You
can turn this on to protect a file.

After you select a file, you can change its attributes—for example,
to *hide* or *protect* the file.

*Hiding and
protecting
files*

1.   Select one or more files whose attributes you want to
     change.

2.   Select Change Attributes from the File menu.

3.   If several files are selected, a window appears, with options
     to (1) change the selected files one at a time, or (2) change
     all selected files at once. Choose either option by clicking
     or by positioning the highlight bar and pressing Enter.

4.   The Change Attribute dialog box (Figure 9.1) appears next.
     To activate or deactivate an attribute, click it with the
     mouse, or highlight it and press the spacebar. (Active at-
     tributes are marked by a ▶.)

5.   Select OK when you've finished assigning attributes.

If you opted to change selected files one at a time (in step 3
above), you'll be prompted to change the attributes for the remaining selected files.

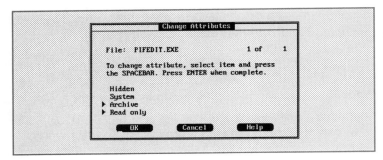

- *Figure 9.1: The Change Attribute dialog box*

ACCESSING DISK, DIRECTORY, AND FILE INFORMATION

DOS maintains certain information about the files, directories, and disks in your system. You can view this information, as described in the following steps:

1. Select any single file name (or directory or disk name).

2. Select Show Information from the Options menu. You'll see a dialog box that displays the information described in Table 9.1.

3. After viewing the Show Information window, click on OK to return to the Shell.

Item	Information Given
File	(Currently selected file)
Name:	Name of currently selected file, or first file in a selected group
Attr:	Attributes assigned (r=read-only; h=hidden; s=system; a=archive)

Table 9.1: Contents of the Show Information Window

Item	Information Given
Selected	**(Drives that have files selected)**
Number:	Number of selected files per drive
Size:	Total bytes used by all selected files (useful for determining how much disk space you'll need to copy or move selected files)
Directory	**(Current directory)**
Name:	Name of the directory
Size:	Bytes stored on the directory
Files:	Number of files on the directory
Disk	**(Selected disk)**
Name:	Volume label of disk (if any)
Size:	Total disk capacity
Avail:	Number of bytes available
Files:	Total number of files stored
Dirs:	Total number of directories

Table 9.1: Contents of the Show Information Window (continued)

Managing the Program List

The Program List window of the Shell lets you maintain a customized list of programs, and run them by double-clicking the program description (or highlighting it and pressing Enter). Initially, the list shows only the Main program group, as shown in Figure 10.1. (If the Task Swapper is disabled, the Program List is the width of the entire screen.) You can add your own programs to the Main group, or create your own groups of programs.

CREATING A NEW PROGRAM GROUP

You can organize several similar programs, like word processors and text editors, into a single group. Then when you select that group, you'll see the commands for starting the programs in it.

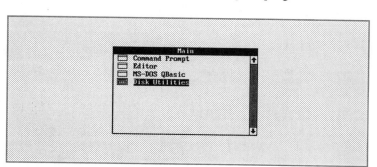

- *Figure 10.1: The Main program group*

To create a new (initially empty) group,

1. Move the highlight bar to the Program List area, and select the Main group (or another group, if desired) as the group to which you are adding.

You see the group name, when you select it, highlighted in the bar at the top of the Program List window. Also, on a graphics monitor, the group names have a special icon.

2. Select New from the File menu.

3. Select Program Group, and then OK. The Add Group dialog box appears.

Group title

4. Type a group title (up to 74 characters). Then press Tab or click on the Help Text box.

Group help text

5. You can type an optional help message, up to 256 characters, into the Help Text box. This text will then appear as context-sensitive help when you press F1 or select Help later, when the group name is highlighted on the Shell.

To start a new line of help text in the dialog box, type an ampersand (&) as the first character in that line.

6. Press Tab, or click on the Password box.

Group password protection

7. If you want to password-protect the group, type a password of up to 256 characters. Only users who know the password will be able to access the group.

8. Select OK.

The new group name now appears in the Main (or current) group.

ADDING A PROGRAM TO A GROUP

Here's how to add a program to a group on the Program List.

1. Select the Main program group, or the group to which you are adding the program (so that the group name appears in the Program List title bar).

2. Select New from the File menu.

3. Select Program Item, and then OK.
4. Type a title, up to 74 characters, that describes the program. (This title will appear in the Program List.)

Program name

5. Press Tab or click the Commands box. There, type the command required to start the program.
6. Select OK (or press Enter).

Testing the Added Program Listing

To test your new program item, select it—by double-clicking, or by highlighting and pressing Enter. If problems arise, refer to "Modifying a Program Item" and "About Properties" later in this Step.

COPYING A PROGRAM FROM A GROUP

If you want to provide access to a program from two or more groups, you can simply copy the program definition from one group to others.

1. Highlight the program name that you want to copy, and select Copy from the File menu.
2. Select the group to which you want to copy the program (the group name appears in the Program List title bar).
3. Press F2.

REARRANGING PROGRAMS AND GROUPS

To change the order of program titles or group titles,

1. Select the group that you want to rearrange.
2. Highlight a title that you want to reposition. (This can be the name of a program or of another group.)
3. Select Reorder from the File menu.
4. Double-click the new location, or highlight it and press Enter.

STEP

10

5. Repeat steps 2 through 4 until the group order is what you want.

DELETING A PROGRAM FROM A GROUP

Follow these simple steps to delete a program from a group:

1. Highlight the program name that you want to delete, and select Delete from the File menu (or press Del).

2. If the program has a password, you'll need to enter it to proceed.

3. Select OK from the confirmation box.

Moving a program item

To move a program from one group to another, first copy it to the new location, and then delete it from its original location.

Deleting a program from a group deletes only the information about that program in the DOSSHELL.INI file (see "About Properties" later in this Step). The program itself remains unchanged on the disk.

DELETING A PROGRAM GROUP

To delete an entire program group, you must first delete (or move) every program item from that group. Then,

1. Highlight the group title that you want to delete, and select Delete from the File menu (or press Del).

2. Select OK.

MODIFYING A GROUP

You can change the title, help text, or password for an existing group.

1. Highlight the group that you want to change, and select Properties from the File menu.

2. Make your changes, and then select OK.

MODIFYING A PROGRAM IN A GROUP

To change a program item definition, you need to change its properties. A program's properties are described in the next section, "About Properties."

1. Select the appropriate group, and highlight the program item you want to change.

2. Select Properties from the File menu. The Program Item Properties dialog box appears, as shown in Figure 10.2. (The box you see will show previous entries.)

3. After making the necessary changes, select OK until you're back to the Shell.

ABOUT PROPERTIES

A program's *properties* are the information that tells the Shell how to run that program. This information is entered in the Program Item Properties dialog box, and is stored in the DOSSHELL.INI file. Every program item on the Program List must have at least two properties: a program title and a startup command. Optional properties include passwords, shortcut keys, and others described in the sections that follow.

```
┌─────────────────────────────────────────┐
│         Program Item Properties          │
│                                          │
│  Program Title . . . . [            ]    │
│                                          │
│  Commands  . . . . . . [          ]  ↖   │
│                                          │
│  Startup Directory . . [          ]      │
│                                          │
│  Application Shortcut Key  (none)        │
│                                          │
│  [ ] Pause after exit    Password . .    │
│                                          │
│   ▄▄OK▄▄   ▄Cancel▄   ▄Help▄  ▄Advanced...▄ │
└─────────────────────────────────────────┘
```

▪ *Figure 10.2: The Program Item Properties dialog box*

Program Title

The program title appears on the Program List. It can be up to 74 characters long; there are no restrictions on spaces or punctuation.

Commands

Commands must include the command(s) that you want DOS to execute when you select the program item.

Finding the program

If the command activates a program whose home directory is not in the current PATH setting, you should precede the command with the program's home directory so that DOS can find the program.

For example, if the startup command for your word processor is WP, and its home directory is C:\WORDS, and if C:\WORDS is not in the PATH setting, then the correct startup command for that program is

```
c:\words\wp
```

Multiple commands

If you want the program item to execute a series of commands, separate the commands with semicolons (;) and at least one blank space. For example, the commands shown next copy all the .BAK files from the current directory to drive A, and then delete them.

```
copy *.bak a: ; erase *.bak
```

Executing batch files

If you want your startup command to execute a DOS batch (.BAT) file, use the CALL command. For example, to run a batch file named CLEANUP.BAT, use one of these startup commands:

```
call cleanup
call c:\batfiles\cleanup
```

Parameters

You can use the *replaceable parameters* 0% through 9% to have your program item present a dialog box before executing its program. For example, you may want DOS to pause for a file name before executing your WP program. To do this, the command and its replaceable parameter would be

```
wp %1
```

When you enter a startup command that includes a replaceable parameter, DOS automatically requests the information listed below. These options define the dialog box that will display whenever you execute the program from the Program List. If you leave these options blank, the generic dialog box is displayed before the program is executed.

Dialog boxes

Window Title: Title in the dialog box title bar

Program Information: First line of text inside the dialog box

Prompt Message: Prompt next to the text box in the dialog box

Default Parameters: Initial text in the text box (optional)

Optional Properties

Startup Directory: If you enter this property, you force DOS to switch to a new directory before executing the program. For example, suppose your WP program is stored on C:\WORD, but you store most documents on C:\WORD\DOCS. As long as C:\WORD is in PATH, you can make C:\WORD\DOCS the startup directory. That way, WP will automatically use C:\WORDS\DOCS as the directory for saving and retrieving files. (Check your program's documentation to make sure it supports this capability.)

Startup Directory

Application Shortcut Key: You can define a shortcut key for getting back into a program after swapping out of it. The shortcut must be a combination keystroke starting with Shift, Alt, or Ctrl. *Press* the keys that you want to use for the shortcut; for example, press Ctrl and W to make Ctrl+W the shortcut. Do not use Ctrl+C, Ctrl+H, Ctrl+I, Ctrl+M, Ctrl+[, or Ctrl+5 (on the numeric keypad), nor Shift+ any of these Ctrl key combinations.

Even if you assign a shortcut key to a program, you still must *start* the program from the Program List by double-clicking or pressing

Enter. However, if the Prevent Program Switching option is off (see end of this Step), and the Task Swapper is currently active, you can swap out of the running program by pressing Alt+Esc. To swap back into the program, you can press your shortcut key.

Pause for a keypress

Pause After Exit: If enabled, this property causes DOS to display the message "Press Any Key To Exit" after exiting the program and before returning to the Shell. If not enabled, exiting the program will take you directly to the Shell.

Password protection

Password: If you want to prevent other users from accessing a program from the Program List, enter a password in the Password box. Anyone attempting to run the program from the Shell will be prompted to first enter the correct password.

Advanced Properties

Selecting the Advanced... command button on the Program Item Properties dialog box takes you to some additional options for defining your program item. These options are shown in Figure 10.3 and described in the sections that follow.

Custom help text

Help Text: Here you can add your own help message, up to 256 characters. This will appear when the user presses F1 while the program item is highlighted, or while its dialog box is displayed.

```
╔══════════════════════════════════════════════╗
║                   Advanced                   ║
║  Help Text  [                             ]  ║
║                                              ║
║  Conventional Memory   KB Required [      ]   ║
║                                              ║
║  XMS Memory  KB Required [      ]  KB Limit [      ] ║
║                                              ║
║  Video Mode  ● Text     Reserve Shortcut Keys [ ] ALT+TAB ║
║              ○ Graphics                   [ ] ALT+ESC  ║
║  [ ] Prevent Program Switch               [ ] CTRL+ESC ║
║        ( OK )        ( Cancel )      ( Help )   ║
╚══════════════════════════════════════════════╝
```

■ *Figure 10.3: Advanced Properties dialog box*

To begin a new line of help text in the window, type an ampersand (&) as the first character of that line.

Conventional Memory KB Required: Enter the minimum amount (kilobytes) of memory that must be available for the program to run. For example, if you enter 380, and then try to run the program later when there is less than 380K available, the Shell informs you of the shortage and will not run the program.

Memory requirements

When you leave this option blank, DOS 5 will try to run the program regardless of how much memory is available. If there is sufficient memory, the program itself returns the "not enough memory" error message.

XMS Memory: Here you determine how the program will use your computer's extended memory.

Extended memory

KB Required   Indicate the program's extended memory requirement. If the program does not specifically require extended memory, leave this option blank.

KB Limit   Specify the maximum extended memory DOS 5 will allocate to the program. If left blank, a default of 384K is allocated (provided the system has at least that much extended memory). Zero (0) prevents the program from using any extended memory, and -1 gives the program as much as it needs (or all that is available, whichever is smaller). Any other number defines the specific maximum extended memory allowed.

Video Mode: Choose between two modes of running the program. *Text* mode requires the least memory. *Graphics* mode requires more memory than Text mode.

Reserve Shortcut Keys: Here you can specify whether or not a keystroke combination activates the Task Swapper, as described in Step 5. For example, normally you use Alt+Tab to activate the Swapper. In another program, however, Alt+Tab might be used to perform some other function, such as display a menu.

To prevent Alt+Tab from activating the Task Swapper, check its box on the Advanced Properties screen. Then when you run a program, Alt+Tab will play the role it has in that program. Unchecked keystroke combinations in the list will continue to activate the Swapper.

Prevent Program Switching: Check this box to altogether disable task swapping from the current program. In this case, the only way out of the program is by exiting.

Customizing the Shell

This Step tells you how to customize the overall appearance of the DOS 5 Shell.

CHOOSING A VIEW

The default *view,* or arrangement, for the Shell is called Program/ File Lists. This view displays the Directory Tree, Files window, and Program List. You can specify other arrangements, through which you select files and menu options just as you would in the default view.

To choose a view,

1. Select View from the menu bar.

2. On the View pull-down menu, choose one of these options:

    Single File List: Displays the Directory Tree and Files window only.

    View options

    Dual File Lists: Lets you access two independent sets of disk drive, Directory Tree, and Files List areas. Useful for selecting files across directories, or viewing files on separate drives.

    All Files: Displays all the files in a directory, and information about the currently highlighted file.

    Program/File Lists: The default display.

    Program List: Displays the Program List only.

Two other options on the View menu let you update the screen.

Repaint Screen: Rewrites the screen without rereading the disk (for example, to remove a network message).

Refresh: Rereads the disk to update the File List (for example, to exclude/include recently deleted and restored files).

Using the Dual File Lists View

When you're using the Dual File Lists view, you can move/copy files by pointing to a file, holding down the mouse button, and dragging the file icon to another drive or directory icon. When you do this, keep in mind the following:

- When you drag a file to another directory on the *same* drive, you're *moving* it; this is the most common reason for dragging a file to a new directory.

- When you drag a file to a directory on a *different* drive, you're *copying* it; this is the most common reason for dragging a file to a new drive.

If you get confused, remember that you can enforce moving or copying by dragging with either Ctrl or Alt held down. Whether you're dragging to the same or a different drive, dragging a file with Ctrl held down is *always* a copy; dragging with Alt held down is *always* a move.

CHANGING THE
APPEARANCE OF TEXT AND GRAPHICS

Depending on your monitor, you may be able to select from several different modes of displaying text and graphics.

1. Select Display... from the Options menu.

2. Use the scroll bar or ↑ and ↓ keys to scroll through the available display modes.

3. Select a display mode by highlighting and pressing Enter, or by double-clicking.

You may want to examine several display modes to see what's available on your monitor, and find the mode that best suits your own taste. You can do this with the Preview command button on the Screen Mode dialog box.

CHANGING THE SHELL COLORS

You can choose any one of several predefined color schemes to change the Shell's "look." You can even add your own color scheme to the available selections (explained later in this Step).

If you're using a mouse,   *Mouse*

1. Click Options in the menu bar, then on Colors... in the pull-down menu, and then double-click on any color combination.

2. Click on the Preview command button to view the color scheme.

3. If you like the color scheme you've chosen, select OK.

Using your keyboard,   *Keyboard*

1. Press and release the Alt (or F10) key.

2. Type the letter *O* to pull down the Options menu.

3. Press ↑ and then Enter to highlight and select Colors...(or just type the letter *O*).

4. Press Tab or Shift+Tab until the cursor is within the list of available color schemes.

5. Press ↑ and ↓ to scroll up and down through available color schemes.

6. To select Preview to preview a color scheme, press Tab twice and then Enter.

7. To select the current color scheme, press Enter. Or press Esc to abandon the operation and keep the original colors.

CREATING YOUR OWN COLOR SCHEMES

You can create your own Shell color schemes by editing the DOSSHELL.INI (DOS Shell Initialization) file with any text editor or word processor that allows you to edit and save ASCII text files. Your color schemes, as well as some predefined ones, all appear on the Options menu for your selection.

In this exercise, we'll use the Editor (it's part of DOS 5) to create a new color scheme. (See Step 15 for more on using the Editor.)

Backing Up DOSSHELL.INI

To play it safe, always make a backup copy of your current working DOSSHELL.INI file prior to changing it. That way, if you make a mistake and disable the file, you can just replace the faulty copy with the previous "healthy" one.

1. Select the drive (typically C) and directory (typically \DOS) where DOSSHELL.INI is stored.

2. Select DOSSHELL.INI from the Files List (by clicking or highlighting the file name).

3. Select Copy from the File menu.

4. Press →, and type **\DOSSHELL.BAK** as the name of the backup file. The To: box will show **C:\DOS\DOSSHELL.BAK**.

5. Press Enter, or click on OK. If asked for confirmation, select Yes.

Now your DOSSHELL.BAK file is an exact duplicate of your working DOSSHELL.INI file.

Editing DOSSHELL.INI

Next you'll use the Editor to access the DOSSHELL.INI file for editing.

1. Select (with mouse or keyboard) the Editor in the Main program group.

2. When prompted, type **C:\DOS\DOSSHELL.INI** as the file name and press Enter (or click OK).

3. To locate the color definitions,

   a. Select Find from the Search menu.

   b. Type **color** (all lowercase) as the word to search for, and choose the Whole Word option.

   c. Select OK.

   This will bring you to the area of DOSSHELL.INI where color definitions are stored. The list begins with

   ```
   color =
   {
   ```

4. To create your own color scheme definition, you need to create an entry within the *colors* = portion of the DOSSHELL.INI file. Look for a section that begins with the *selection* = commands, and ends with two curly braces on separate lines. For example, Figure 11.1 shows the Basic Blue definition.

The easiest way to create a new color scheme is to make a copy of an existing color scheme, and then change its title and color definitions. To do so,

5. Move the cursor (and mouse pointer if you have one) to the left edge of the screen, next to the *selection* = command for a color scheme.

6. Select the *entire* color scheme definition. Hold down the mouse button and scroll to the end of the definition; or hold down the Shift key and scroll with the ↓ key. Select all the way to the last } above the *selection* = command for the next color definition.

7. Release the mouse button, and select Copy from the Edit menu (or press Ctrl+Ins).

8. Move the cursor to the start of any other color definition (for instance, to the left of the *selection* = line for the Ocean color definition).

```
selection =
{
    title = Basic Blue
    foreground =
    {
        base = black
        highlight = brightwhite
        selection = brightwhite
        alert = brightred
        menubar = black
        menu = black
        disabled = white
        accelerator = cyan
        dialog = black
        button = black
        elevator = white
        titlebar = black
        scrollbar = brightwhite
        borders = black
        drivebox = black
        driveicon = black
        cursor = black
    }
    background =
    {
        base = brightwhite
        highlight = blue
        selection = black
        alert = brightwhite
        menubar = white
        menu = brightwhite
        disabled = brightwhite
        accelerator = brightwhite
        dialog = brightwhite
        button = white
        elevator = white
        titlebar = white
        scrollbar = black
        borders = brightwhite
        drivebox = brightwhite
        driveicon = brightwhite
        cursor = brightblack
    }
}
```

■ *Figure 11.1: A color scheme definition within DOSSHELL.INI*

9. Press Enter to insert a blank line.

10. Press ↑ to move the cursor to the blank line.

11. Select Paste from the Edit menu (or press Shift+Ins).

12. Change the title (next to *title =*) to whatever name you have chosen for your new color scheme.

13. Next you must assign colors to the foreground and background of the screen areas in Table 11.1. Use the valid color names listed below. Notice that the foreground and background colors are defined in separate parts of the DOSSHELL.INI file (*foreground =* and *background =*).

black	brightblack
blue	brightblue
brown	brightyellow
cyan	brightcyan
green	brightgreen
magenta	brightmagenta
red	brightred
white	brightwhite

14. Save your new color scheme by selecting Exit from the File menu, and answering **Yes** when asked about saving the file.

To test the new color scheme, preview it in the Colors... menu, as described in "Changing the Shell Colors" earlier in this Step.

You should fully exit the Shell (press F3), and then return to it (enter **DOSSHELL**) to make sure you didn't make a mistake that renders the DOSSHELL.INI file unusable. If you can't get the Shell running from the command prompt, copy your working DOSSHELL.BAK file to DOSSHELL.INI, with

```
COPY C:\DOS\DOSSHELL.BAK C:\DOS\DOSSHELL.INI
```

so that you can get the Shell started again.

Shell area names

Name in DOSSHELL.INI	Area of Shell
base	Directory Tree, Files Area, Program List, and Task Swapper
highlight	Highlighted or selected items, and Shell title bar
selection	Activated options
alert	Warning message windows
menubar	Selected menus
menu	Menu bar, unselected menus, and status line
disabled	Dimmed menu options
accelerator	Underlined letters in menu options
dialog	Dialog boxes
button	Dialog box command buttons
elevator	Scroll box
titlebar	Area title bars
scrollbar	Slider bars
borders	Dialog box borders
drivebox	Disk drive area
driveicon	Disk drive icon
cursor	The cursor

Table 11.1: Areas of the Shell That You Can Color

Using the Command Prompt

Like earlier versions of DOS, version 5 also offers the command prompt as an alternate user interface. This Step assumes that you're already familiar with your computer, and therefore also familiar with basic DOS commands. So let's just briefly review the basics of issuing commands to DOS 5 from the command prompt rather than through the Shell.

ACCESSING THE COMMAND PROMPT

To get to the command prompt, you have to leave the Shell. There are two ways to do this.

- You can remove the Shell from memory, which cancels all current selections but gives you access to all of your computer's memory. Or…

- You can temporarily leave the Shell, which retains current settings but leaves a copy of the Shell in memory.

You cannot fully exit the Shell while tasks are running in the Task Swapper—you must first exit each program in the Swapper. You can, however, exit the Shell temporarily while tasks are still running.

Full Exit from the Shell

To leave the Shell and remove it from memory, use either your mouse or the keyboard.

Full exit

85

- With a mouse, select Exit from the File menu, by clicking first on File in the menu bar, and then Exit in the pull-down menu.

- On the keyboard, simply press F3 or, Alt+F4.

Returning to Shell   To return to the Shell after a full exit, type **DOSSHELL** and press Enter.

Temporary Exit from the Shell

Temporary exit   To leave the Shell temporarily, without losing any current settings or tasks,

- Press Shift+F9, or select Command Prompt from the Program List.

Return to Shell   To return to the Shell from a temporary exit, with your previous settings intact,

1. Type **EXIT** and press Enter.

2. If prompted, press any key to get to the Shell.

If you use **DOSSHELL** to run the Shell after a temporary exit, you'll actually load a second copy of the Shell. Therefore, if you can't remember how you last exited the Shell, try an **EXIT** command first.

ENTERING COMMANDS

The command prompt is just the name of the current drive and directory, followed by a greater-than sign and a blinking cursor. For example, if you're on the DOS directory of drive C, you'll see

```
C:\DOS>_
```

To enter a command at the prompt,

1. Type the complete command. Use Backspace, ← or → to make necessary corrections.

2. Press Enter to complete the command.

DOS 5 does not distinguish between uppercase and lowercase letters; you can use either or both when typing a command.

Using Command Parameters

Command *parameters* generally tell DOS what disk drive, directory, and/or files to use. Parameters are often optional; if they are omitted, DOS assumes you mean the current drive and directory. For example, the command DIR lists all the files on the current drive and directory, but DIR A:\ lists file names from the root directory of drive A. Parameters are always preceded by a blank space.

Switches

Many commands also let you use *switches* to further refine how the command operates. A switch is a forward slash (/) followed by a single letter or word. Switches are always the last items in a command.

As an example, the DIR command provides a /w switch, which widens the list of filenames.

```
dir /w
```

If you add both a parameter and the /w switch, type the switch last, and precede it with a space.

```
dir a:/ \w
```

GETTING HELP WITH COMMANDS

You can get help with any command by entering that command with the /? switch, for example,

```
dir /?
```

Optionally, you can enter **Help,** followed by a blank space and the command you need help with, as in

```
help dir
```

The resulting help display includes a brief description of the command, its syntax, and any available parameters and switches. Optional parameters and switches are shown in brackets; if you do elect to use an optional parameter or switch, don't type the brackets.

CANCELING A COMMAND

To interrupt an executing command, press Ctrl+C or Ctrl+Break.

REPEATING AND EDITING COMMANDS

When you need to repeat or modify a command you just entered, you can use the keys listed in Table 12.1 to help out.

Key	Effect
F1 or →	Recalls one character
F3	Recalls the entire previous command
Delete (Del)	Deletes the character at the cursor from the previous command
Backspace or ←	Deletes the character to the left of the cursor, and moves back a character
Insert (Ins)	Inserts the next characters you type at the current cursor position
F2	Retypes all characters of the last command, up to and including the next character you type
F4	Pressing F4, then a letter, and then F3, retypes that letter and the remaining characters from the previous command

Table 12.1: Keys Used to Edit Commands

DOS normally allows you to recall only the last command entered, but with the DOSKey option you can recall many preceding commands. You'll read about DOSKey in Step 14.

INTERNAL AND EXTERNAL COMMANDS

There are two classes of DOS commands.

Internal commands are stored in memory, and are therefore accessible at any time.

External commands are stored in a file on disk, and are accessible only if DOS can find them.

Tables 12.2 and 12.3 list internal and external commands and the basic tasks they perform. You will recognize that many of the jobs performed by these commands are available from the Shell and have already been described in this book. Other actions are described in later Steps.

To augment the brief command descriptions you see here, you can get immediate help by using the /? switch or **help** along with the command, as described earlier in this Step. You can also enter **help** alone, to get a list of commands and what they do. Or refer to the DOS 5 User's Guide.

Command	Purpose
BREAK	Enable/disable Ctrl+C
CD or CHDIR	Change the directory
CHCP	Change the code page
CLS	Clear the screen
COPY	Copy a file
CTTY	Use a teletype device for input
DATE	Change the system date
DEL	Delete a file

Table 12.2: Internal DOS 5 Commands

Command	Purpose
DIR	Show file names
ERASE	Delete a file
EXIT	Return to the Shell or the running program
MD or MKDIR	Create a directory
PATH	Define directories to search for programs
RD or RMDIR	Remove a directory
SET	View/change the environment
TIME	Change the system time
TRUENAME	Display the real name of a drive, after an ASSIGN or SUBST command
TYPE	Display the contents of a file
VER	Display current DOS version
VERIFY	Activate/deactivate copy verification

Table 12.2: Internal DOS 5 Commands (continued)

Command	Purpose
APPEND	Define directories to search for non-program files
ASSIGN	Assign a new letter-name to a drive
ATTRIB	Display/change file attributes
BACKUP	Back up files on a hard disk
CHKDSK	Check a disk and display a status report
COMMAND	Start a new command processor
COMP	Compare the contents of two files
DEBUG	Start the DOS debugging program
DISKCOMP	Compare two floppy disks

Table 12.3: External DOS 5 Commands

Command	Purpose
DISKCOPY	Copy a floppy disk
DOSKEY	Store commands in a buffer and create macros
DOSSHELL	Activate the DOS 5 Shell
EDIT	Activate the DOS 5 screen editor
EDLIN	Activate the DOS line editor
EMM386	Enable/disable 80386 expanded memory emulation
EXE2BIN	Convert an .EXE file to binary
FASTOPEN	Activate a secondary disk cache
FC	Compare two files and report differences
FDISK	Configure a hard disk for use with DOS 5
FIND	Search for text in a file or command output
FORMAT	Format a disk
GRAFTABL	Load a set of graphics characters
GRAPHICS	Let a printer display a graphics screen
JOIN	Join a disk drive to a directory on another drive
KEYB	Load a foreign language character set
LABEL	Show/change a disk's volume label
LOADHIGH	Load a program into high memory
MEM	Display current memory status
MIRROR	Record information for REBUILD and UN DELETE
MODE	Configure devices
MORE	Display output one screen at a time

Table 12.3: External DOS 5 Commands (continued)

Command	Purpose
NLSFUNC	Support foreign language code page switching
PRINT	Print text files in the background
QBASIC	Run the QBasic program
REBUILD	"Unformat" an accidentally formatted disk
RECOVER	Recover data from a bad disk
RESTORE	Restore files saved with BACKUP
SETVER	Display/modify the DOS version table
SHARE	Enables file sharing and locking
SORT	Sort the contents of a file or screen display
SUBST	Change a path name to a drive name
SYS	Copy system tracks and hidden system files
TREE	Display the Directory Tree
UNDELETE	Undelete a file deleted with DEL or ERASE
VOL	Display a disk's volume label
XCOPY	A more powerful version of COPY

Table 12.3: External DOS 5 Commands (continued)

Changing drives You may have noticed that there is no command for selecting a disk drive. You accomplish that by simply entering the drive's letter-name at the prompt.

ENTERING COMMANDS IN THE SHELL

Instead of leaving the Shell to enter a command, you can select Run from the File pull-down menu, type any valid DOS command, and then press Enter (or select OK). When the command finishes its job, you'll be returned to the Shell.

Piping
and Redirection

Normally, DOS expects input to come from your keyboard or mouse, and then displays its output on the screen. However, you can redirect the input and output of virtually every DOS command.

REDIRECTING INPUT AND OUTPUT

These symbols are used for redirecting input and output.

> Sends output to named device or file

\>> Appends output to named file

< Accepts input from named command or file

¦ Transfers output from one command to another (called a *pipe*)

Device names are the DOS names for the ports to which the devices are attached. Examples are PRN (the current printer), LPT1 (the first parallel printer port), and COM1 (the first serial port).

To completely suppress the output normally displayed by a command, send its output to the NUL device.

Suppressing output

Output to a File

This command stores file names from the root directory in a file named filelist.txt:

Sending to a file

```
dir c:\ >filelist.txt
```

93

*Adding
to a file*

This command adds the file names from the C:\DOS directory to the file named filelist.txt:

```
dir c:\dos >>filelist.txt
```

Output to a Printer

The following command prints the results of the DIR command:

```
dir >prn
```

This command prints a copy of the entire Directory Tree:

```
tree \ >prn
```

When you're using a laser printer, printed copy may not appear until the page is filled and ejected. To eject a page on most printers you can use this command (press Ctrl+L to type the ^L symbol):

```
echo ^L>prn
```

Printing "Screen Dumps"

To print a copy of whatever is currently on your screen, press the Print Screen (PrtSc) key (or Shift+PrtSc on some computers). If you are viewing a graphics screen and don't have a graphics printer, you'll likely see foreign language characters in place of the graphics image you expect. You may also need to eject the page.

*Printer
slaving*

You can also "*slave*" the printer, that is, make it repeat whatever appears on the screen. Press Ctrl+P to initiate printer slaving, and then Ctrl+P again when you want to end it.

Background Printing

Another way to print text files is with the PRINT command, which lets you continue to use your computer while the printer is doing its job. However, because the PRINT program is partially memory resident, you need to be careful not to load it while other programs are suspended.

Your safest bet is to preload the memory-resident portion of PRINT by using the /d switch with PRINT in your AUTO-EXEC.BAT file. This switch defines the printer device, which can be the default port (PRN), or any parallel port (LPT*n*), or any serial port (COM*n*). It then loads the resident portion of PRINT, but does not request the files to be printed. Here's an example.

*Preloading
PRINT*

```
print /d:prn
```

Later in the work session, you can then print any file by entering the PRINT command followed by the file name or pattern, as in these examples:

```
print letter1.txt
print letter*.txt
```

ABOUT FILTERS

Filters are DOS programs that receive data from another command or program, and alter that data or its appearance. Typically you use *pipes* to separate the programs in the command line. The MORE command is a filter that causes a command to output its data one screen at a time. For example, to view the contents of filelist.txt, one screen at a time, you might use

*MORE
command*

```
type filelist.txt >prn
```

Or, just direct the contents of a file into the command.

```
more < filelist.txt
```

Finding Text

The FIND command is a filter that limits output to lines that contain specific text, and can also be used to search the contents of files. To use it as a means of controlling printed output, pipe output to it. For example, the following command restricts the output

*FIND
command*

of the DIR command to only lines that contain a colon:

```
dir | find ":"
```

To have FIND search the contents of files, type the text you want to look for, followed by the names of files to search (wildcards are *not* permitted). For example, this command searches Let1.txt, Let2.txt, and Let3.txt for "January 31":

```
find "January 31" Let1.txt Let2.txt Let3.txt
```

You can also redirect the results of a FIND command to the printer or to a file, by placing the usual > or >> characters at the end of the command.

Sorting Text

The third filter is SORT, which rearranges the text in a file, or the text from a command. This next command displays file names from the DIR command in alphabetical order:

```
dir | sort
```

SORT supports these switches:

/r   reverses the sort order (for example, in order from Z to A, or from largest to smallest)

/+n sorts starting at the characters defined by n in each line

For example, the DIR command displays the size of each file next to each file name, starting at about the 13th character on the line. The command

```
dir | sort /+13
```

lists file names sorted by file size. This next command does the same, but it reverses the order—displaying files in largest-to-smallest order, rather than smallest-to-largest:

```
dir | sort /+13 /r
```

You can combine filters in a command. For instance, this command displays files in reverse size order, and limits the display to file names (all of which have a colon embedded in the time column):

```
dir | sort /+13 /r | find ":"
```

Here is an example of sorting the contents of a file. It takes text from a file named random.txt, and writes it to a file named sorted.txt, in sorted order.

```
sort < random.txt >sorted.txt
```

Sorting the DIR Display

In preceding examples we've used the DIR command only as an example of using SORT. Keep in mind, also, that DIR offers the /o switch, which you can follow with any combination of the sort order options n (name), e (extension), s (size), or d (date). Precede a letter with a minus sign to reverse the sort order. For example, this command lists file names sorted in ascending (earliest-to-latest) date order:

```
dir /od
```

and this command lists file names in reverse (latest-to-earliest) date order:

```
dir /o -d
```

Using DOSKey

The DOSKey feature is new in version 5 of DOS. This feature records in a *buffer* (an area in memory) commands you enter at the command prompt. You can then redisplay and reexecute or modify the recorded commands. DOSKey also lets you put multiple commands on a single line, and design *macros*—internal, personalized commands that you create yourself.

INSTALLING DOSKEY

To activate DOSKey,

- Enter **doskey** at the command prompt.

After you press Enter, the message "DOSKey installed" appears. DOSKey automatically reserves 512 bytes of memory for recording your commands. When the buffer is filled, the oldest command is removed to make room for the newest one.

If you want to set aside more or less than 512 bytes for the buffer, use the /bufsize= switch. The following command sets aside 1K of buffer space for DOSKey:

Changing the buffer size

```
doskey /bufsize=1024
```

If you've already activated DOSKey, but want to reinstall it (perhaps to change the buffer size), use the /reinstall switch. For example:

The /reinstall switch

```
doskey /reinstall /bufsize=2048
```

99

Using /reinstall deletes all commands from the buffer.

REUSING COMMANDS

To reuse a recorded command, you simply redisplay it (and, optionally, change it), and press Enter to execute it. Tables 14.1 and 14.2 list keys used to redisplay and change commands recorded with DOSKey.

Key	Function
↑	Scrolls backward through recorded commands
↓	Scrolls forward through recorded commands
PgUp	Displays the first command in the buffer
PgDn	Displays the last command in the buffer
F7	Displays all commands in the buffer
*text*F8	Searches for commands that start with the *text* you specify
F9	Lets you recall a command by its *number*
Alt+F7	Deletes all commands from the buffer
Alt+F10	Deletes all current macros

Table 14.1: Keys Used with DOSKey

Key	Function
← and →	Positions the cursor to any character in the command
Home	Moves to the start of the command
End	Moves to the end of the command
Ctrl+ ←	Moves back one word
Ctrl+ →	Moves forward one word

Table 14.2: Keys Used to Edit Commands in DOSKey

Key	Function
Backspace	Deletes the character to the left of the cursor
Delete (Del)	Deletes the character at the cursor
Ctrl+End	Deletes all characters from the cursor to the end of the line
Ctrl+Home	Deletes all characters from the cursor to the beginning of the line
Ins	Inserts new typed characters at cursor position
Esc	Erases the currently displayed command

Table 14.2: Keys Used to Edit Commands in DOSKey (continued)

ENTERING MULTIPLE COMMANDS

With DOSKey installed, you can also type and execute multiple commands on a single line, up to a maximum of 127 characters. To do so, just press Ctrl+T between each command. A paragraph symbol (¶) appears where you press Ctrl+T. For example, to clear the screen and change the system date and time, you can enter this command:

```
cls ¶ date ¶ time
```

where ¶ is typed by pressing Ctrl+T. When you press Enter, each command will be executed.

ABOUT MACROS

A *macro* is sort of a "large command" with a name, that actually executes several commands. In this sense, macros are much like batch files (Step 16). There are, however, many differences between macros and batch files.

■ Macros are stored in memory rather than on disk. This means they run a little faster, but they also disappear the moment you turn off the computer.

Macros vs. batch files

- Macros have all their commands on one line, whereas a batch file consists of many commands on separate lines. Multiple commands in macros are separated by $T or $t.

- A macro cannot exceed 127 characters, but there's no limit to the length of a batch file.

- You can terminate a batch file by pressing Ctrl+C or Ctrl+Break once, but in a macro these keys terminate only the current command.

- The replaceable parameters in macros are $1 through $9, rather than the %1 and %9 of batch files. In addition, macros use unique characters for piping and redirection (see Table 14.3).

Character	Macro Equivalent	Purpose
<	$L or $l	Redirects input
>	$G or $g	Redirects output
>>	$GG or $gg	Appends output to a file
¦	$B or $b	Redirects output from one command to another

Table 14.3: Redirection Characters Used in Macros

- In macros, you cannot use the common GOTO and ECHO OFF batch file commands.

- Neither a batch file nor another macro can *start* a macro. A macro may, however, start a batch file; and a batch file may *create* macros.

Creating Macros

To create a macro, you install DOSKey with the macro name, followed by an equal sign and the commands you want the macro to execute.

A handy macro

Let's start with a simple example. Suppose you're tired of entering DOSSHELL as the command to start the Shell from the command prompt. You can create a macro that lets you start the Shell with just the letter *d*. To do so, enter this command to create a macro named **D**:

```
doskey D= dosshell
```

For the remainder of the current session (until you turn off the computer), you'll be able to bring up the Shell by simply typing the letter *d* and pressing Enter at the command prompt. (Later in this Step, we'll discuss ways of making macros more permanent.)

Here's an example of a more advanced macro named Search. It searches all the directories on hard drives C and D for a specific file (or type of file).

A search macro

```
doskey search=dir c:\$1 /s $t dir d:\$1 /s
```

Notice that two DIR commands will be executed by the macro, one starting at the root directory of drive C (dir c:\), and the other starting at the root directory of drive D (dir d:\). In each DIR command, $1 is a replaceable parameter, and /s is an optional switch that tells DIR to search subdirectories.

Executing a Macro

To execute a macro, type its name and press Enter. If you've included replaceable parameters, include in the command the data for the parameters, each preceded by a blank space. For example, to have the Search macro look for files that match the pattern QTR?.TAX, enter

```
search qtr?.tax
```

If you give a macro the same name as another DOS command or program, DOS will execute the macro only. However, when you press the spacebar before typing a command, DOS does not even look for a macro. For example, the command shown below creates a macro named Type. This macro displays the contents of a file, as does the internal TYPE command; but the macro pauses for a keypress after each screenful of data.

Naming macros

```
doskey type= type $1 $b more
```

Whenever you enter the Type command, this macro will automatically be executed, pausing at each screenful of file data. If you precede a Type command with a blank space, however, this macro is ignored, and the normal internal TYPE command is executed.

Displaying Existing Macros

To view a list of all the currently available macros, enter

```
doskey /macros
```

Editing a Macro

When you create a macro, DOS stores that command in the buffer. Therefore, to edit an existing macro, press ↑ (or any other redisplay key from Table 14.1) to bring the macro back to the command prompt. Then edit the macro with the editing keys (Table 14.2), and press Enter to execute the modified command.

Saving Macros

Turning off the computer erases all macros from memory, but you *can* save your macro names and commands—in a batch file. You'll need to modify that file slightly (as described in this section), but after you do, you can re-create all of your macros just by running the batch file.

To copy current macro definitions from memory to a file, use the /macros switch (which you abbreviate as /m) and the >> redirection symbol. For example, you might enter the command

```
doskey /macros >>c:\dos\macros.bat
```

to copy all current macro definitions to MACROS.BAT on C:\DOS. If you then use the Editor (Step 15) to edit that file, you'll see new macros listed in this format:

```
SEARCH=dir c:\$1 /s $t dir d:\$1 /s
```

To make this a valid command for creating a macro, simply type **doskey** and a blank space in front of the macro name, like this:

```
doskey D=dosshell
doskey SEARCH=dir c:\$1 /s $t dir d:\$1 /s
```

Make sure every macro name in the new batch file is preceded by DOSKey and a blank space, and then save the file again with the same name. At any time in the future, you can re-create all your macros simply by entering the command **MACROS** (or **C:\DOS\MACROS**) to execute the batch file. Or, just place the CALL MACROS command in your AUTOEXEC.BAT file (described in Step 17) to create the macros automatically at startup.

Your macros may contain control or other special characters, like the Ctrl+L in

Special characters in macros

```
doskey ff=echo ^L $G prn
```

which will eject the printer page when you enter FF. When this macro is redirected to a file, the ^L control character may be converted to an actual caret and letter *L*. See "Special Characters" in Chapter 15 for advice on correcting this problem.

The $* Parameter

In macros, the $* parameter is different from the parameters $1 through $9; $* ignores the blank spaces sent from the command line, which normally separate these parameters. Use $* when you want to send an unknown number of $*n* parameters to a macro.

For instance, when using the Search macro, you can send only one parameter (a file name or pattern), as in **search *.bak**. If you enter additional parameters, as **in search *.bak /b**, Search ignores the second parameter (/b), because of the blank space that precedes it.

The blank space causes the /b to be treated as $2, which is not de-fined in the Search macro.

However, consider the use of the $* parameter, rather than $1, in this Search macro:

```
doskey SEARCH=dir c:\$* /s $t dir d:\$* /s
```

Here you can indeed enter a command like **search *.bak /b**, or **search *.let /b /w**, because DOS ignores the blank spaces separat-ing the parameter and switches, and replaces the $* parameter with all of the text to the right of the Search command.

Batch File Commands in Macros

Although you cannot use the GOTO or ECHO OFF commands in a macro, you can use other common batch file commands. Type a $t symbol to mark the start of each new command. For example, to make the Search macro pause for a keypress before searching the next drive, insert the PAUSE command, like this:

```
doskey SEARCH=dir c:\$* /s $t pause $t dir
d:\$* /s
```

Deleting a Macro

To delete a macro from memory and reclaim the space it occupies, enter the DOSKey command followed by the macro name and an = sign. For example, to delete the Search macro, enter the follow-ing command:

```
doskey search=
```

To delete *all* macro definitions, press Alt+F10.

Using EDIT

DOS 5's new screen editor is called EDIT, and replaces the archaic "teletype" editor, Edlin, of previous versions. You can use EDIT to create and change batch files, as well as small text files like lists and notes.

STARTING EDIT
To start EDIT from the Shell,

1. With your mouse or from the keyboard, select Editor from the Main group in the Program List.

2. When prompted, type the path and name of the file you want to edit (for example, **c:\dos\myfile.txt**). Then press Enter or click on OK.

Or, if you are working from the command prompt, enter the **Edit** command followed by the path and name of the file you want to edit.

```
edit c:\dos\myfile.txt
```

You can omit the file name in either of the preceding startup commands. This makes EDIT start with a dialog box (Figure 15.1) that asks if you want to see the Survival Guide (help system) first, or go straight to the editing screen.

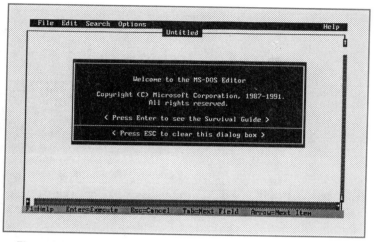

- *Figure 15.1: The Editor welcome screen*

BASIC MENU AND HELP OPERATIONS

Your interface with the Editor works similarly to that of the Shell. Once you are inside the Editor, the main keys are

Alt: Activates the menu bar, where you select menu commands with your mouse, or the usual arrow keys and Enter.

F1: Accesses online help. Selectable topics are displayed between ◄ and ► symbols. To choose a topic, click it with your mouse, or move the cursor to it (with Tab or Shift+Tab) and press Enter. (Notice also the functions available in the action bar near the bottom of the screen.) Press Esc to leave help.

F6: While a help screen is displayed, pressing F6 switches between the help and editing screens, without removing the help screen.

Esc: Leaves the current window or dialog box without making a selection.

Mouse Button: Click on any menu option or key definition, such as <F1=Help>, to select it.

Typing in the Editor

To type in the Editor, just type as you normally do. Press Enter at the end of each line. (Unlike a word processor, EDIT offers no automatic word wrap, because EDIT isn't designed for working with paragraphs.)

Keys Used for Editing

Table 15.1 lists keys for moving the cursor and scrolling through text in the Editor. These keys work *only* with existing text. For example, when you need to create a new blank line below the last existing line of text, press Enter, not ↓. Or, to move to an empty area to the right of existing text, use the spacebar, not →.

Key	Purpose
Mouse click	Move cursor to mouse pointer
↑, ↓, ←, →	Move one character or line at a time
Ctrl+ ←	Move left one word
Ctrl+ →	Move right one word
Home	Move to start of line
End	Move to end of line
Page Up (PgUp)	Move forward one screen
Page Down (PgDn)	Move backward one screen
Ctrl+Enter	Move to start of next line
Ctrl+QE	Move to top of screen
Ctrl+QX	Move to bottom of screen
Ctrl+Home *or* Ctrl+QR	Move to top of file
Ctrl+End *or* Ctrl+QC	Move to bottom of file
Ctrl+W *or* Ctrl+ ↑	Scroll up a line

Table 15.1: Cursor Movement and Scroll Keys in EDIT

Key	Purpose
Ctrl+Z *or* Ctrl+ ↓	Scroll down a line
Ctrl+Page Up	Scroll to the right one screen
Ctrl+Page Down	Scroll to the left one screen

Table 15.1: Cursor Movement and Scroll Keys in EDIT (continued)

You can also scroll left and right, and up and down through a file using the scroll bars at the right and bottom of the editing window. These work like the vertical scroll bars you've seen in the other DOS 5 windows. However, the following keys behave differently:

Home	Moves all the way to the left
End	Moves all the way to the right
Ctrl+Home	Moves to the top of the document
Ctrl+End	Moves to the end of the document

To edit text in the Editor, use the keys defined in Table 15.2.

Key	Purpose
Backspace *or* Ctrl+H	Delete character to left of cursor
Delete *or* Ctrl+G	Delete character at the cursor
Ctrl+T	Delete from cursor to the end of word
Insert *or* Ctrl+V modes	Switch between Insert and Overwrite
Ctrl+Y	Delete entire line
Ctrl+QY	Delete from cursor to end of line

Table 15.2: Editing Keys in EDIT

Changing Screen Colors

To change the colors on the Editor screen,

1. Select Display... from the Editor's Options menu.

2. Choose foreground and background colors from the dialog box that appears (or press F1 for help).

3. Select OK.

BLOCKING AND EDITING TEXT

One of the handiest features of a screen editor is the ability to se-lect any block of text (by highlighting it), and then move, copy, or delete that block of text.

To block text with your mouse, *Mouse*

1. Point to the first character of text you want to select.

2. Drag the pointer to the last character you want to select.

3. Release the mouse button to block the text.

If you want to unblock the text or redefine the block, click any-where on the Edit screen to "unselect" the block.

To block text using the keyboard, *Keyboard*

1. Move the cursor to the first character of text you want to select.

2. Holding down the Shift key, use the arrow keys to move the cursor to the last character you want to select.

3. Release the Shift and arrow keys.

To cancel the selection, press any arrow key.

Moving Text

To move the currently selected block of text,

1. Select Cut from the Edit menu, or press Shift+Del. The blocked text is removed and hidden in the *Clipboard,* an area in memory that holds a copy of text that's currently being moved or copied.

2. Move the cursor to where you want to reposition the hidden text.

3. Select Paste from the Edit menu, or press Shift+Ins.

Copying Text

To copy the currently selected block of text,

1. Select Copy from the Edit menu, or press Ctrl+Ins.

2. Move the cursor to the location for the copied text.

3. Select Paste from the Edit menu, or press Shift+Ins.

Deleting Text

To delete the currently selected block of text,

■ Select Clear from the Edit menu, or press Del.

SEARCH AND FIND

To locate a particular word or phrase in your text file,

1. Position the cursor where you want to begin the search (only text *below* the cursor position will be searched).

2. Select Find... from the Search menu. The Find dialog box appears (Figure 15.2).

3. Type the text you want to search for.

4. To make your search even more specific,

Narrowing
the search

■ Check the Match Upper/Lowercase box if you want to find only text with matching upper/lowercase letters.

■ Check the Whole Word box if you want to find only whole-word matches. For example, "act" will match "act," but not "actress."

5. Select OK.

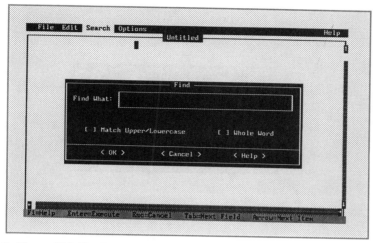

- *Figure 15.2: The Find dialog box*

6. To search for the next occurrence of this text, select Repeat Last Find from the Search menu, or press F3, until you find the text you're looking for.

SEARCH AND REPLACE

You can replace a particular word or phrase throughout your document, as follows:

1. Move the cursor to where you want to start replacing text.

2. Select Change from the Search menu. The Change dialog box appears (Figure 15.3).

3. Type the text you want to replace, and press Tab.

4. Type the replacement (new) text. Or, leave this box blank if you want to delete the replaced (old) text altogether, throughout the document. Then press Tab.

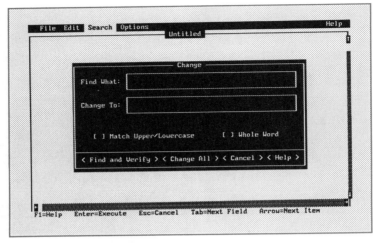

• *Figure 15.3: The Change dialog box*

5. To make your text replacement even more specific,

   ■ Check Match Upper/Lowercase if you want to replace only text that matches the upper/lowercase pattern of the new text.

   ■ Check Whole Word if you want to replace only matching whole words.

Confirming replace-ments

6. If you want to double-check each replacement before it occurs, select Find and Verify. Otherwise, select Change All. With Find and Verify, you'll have the option to change or skip the text each time a match is found.

7. When you're finished with all the replacements, select OK from the Change Complete dialog box that appears.

If you select (block) text on the Editor screen *before* selecting Find or Change, that text automatically appears as the search text in the dialog box.

PRINTING THE FILE

To print all (or some) of the file being edited,

1. If you want to print only a portion of the text, select that text.

2. Select Print from the File menu.

3. If prompted, choose either Selected Text Only or Complete Document.

4. Select OK.

SPECIAL CHARACTERS

If you want to type a control character or other special character while using the Editor,

1. Position the cursor.

2. Press Ctrl+P.

3. Hold down the Alt key, and type the character's ASCII code on the numeric keypad—*not* on the number keys at the top of the keyboard. Then release the Alt key.

For example, to type the Ctrl+L (^L) in the Echo ^L $g prn macro described in Steps 13 and 14, press and release Ctrl+P. Then hold down Alt, type **012** on the numeric keypad, and release Alt. (We knew to type **012** in this example because L is the twelfth letter of the alphabet.)

When the proper control character is in place, the Editor shows the actual character (the Greek female symbol in this case), rather than the ^L character displayed by DOS.

SAVING AND EXITING

There are several ways to save your edited document; you can also choose to stay in or leave the Editor. These choices are all selected from the File menu.

New: Lets you save the current file (if necessary), and then clears it from the screen.

Open: Prompts you to load a new file, and lets you save the current file (if necessary).

Saves: Saves the current file and leaves it on the screen.

Save As: Lets you save the current version of the file with a new name, so that the original file remains unchanged.

Exit: Lets you save the current file (if any), and then exits to the command prompt or Shell.

Specifying path and file name

When saving a file with a new name, you can select a disk drive and directory from the dialog box that appears; or you can select [..] to move up one level in the directory tree; or you can just type the drive and directory name that you want. If you do not specify a drive and directory, DOS assumes you want the current drive and directory. If you do not specify a file name, the file is named Untitled, and will be overwritten the next time you save an un-named file.

EXITING THE EDITOR

To return to the Shell or command prompt from EDIT, and either save or abandon a new or edited file,

1. Select Exit from the File menu.

2. If the current file is new or has been edited, but not yet saved, select Yes to save it now, or No to abandon recent changes.

Creating Batch Files

ABOUT BATCH FILES

Batch files are collections of DOS commands that can be run like programs. You can use them to simplify your work, by combining a series of frequently used commands in a single file.

For example, suppose you regularly copy all your word process- *A sample* ing files (.WP and .LET) to backup files with the .BAK extension. *batch file* You might logically store all those files in a directory named C:\WP\DOCS. Rather than entering the individual commands to make these copies each time you need a backup, you could create a batch file that will enter these commands for you. For example, consider a batch file named WPBAK.BAT, which contains

```
c:
cd\wp\docs
copy *.wp *.bak
copy *.let *.bak
```

With this file stored on disk, whenever you want to perform your backup procedure, you can simply enter **wpbak** at the command prompt, or run the WPBAK.BAT program from the Shell. DOS will execute each command in that file, top to bottom, thus saving you all those steps.

117

CREATING A BATCH FILE

You can use any text editor, including the Editor, to create or edit a batch file. When assigning names to batch files,

- Follow normal file-naming conventions, with no spaces or punctuation in the file name, and always use a .BAT extension.

- If you want easy access to your file, store it in a directory listed in the current PATH statement.

RUNNING BATCH FILES

Once you've created a batch file, you can run it like any program, either by entering its name at the command prompt, or by running it from the Shell using any of the techniques described in Step 5.

PROGRAMMING A BATCH FILE

You can use any DOS command (see Step 12) in any batch file. In addition, there are several programming language-like commands that can add flexibility to your batch files (and macros). Of interest mainly to experienced programmers, these commands are summarized here in Step 16. If you plan to use them, study your DOS documentation for the most complete details and instructions.

Programmer Comments

REM
command

Programmers use comments to write notes and messages into batch files and other programs. The REM command marks the beginning of a programmer comment, and the end of the line marks the end of the comment.

Hiding and Displaying Messages

ECHO
command

ECHO is used to control whether batch file commands are displayed on the screen as they are executed. The command ECHO OFF suppresses echoing; ECHO ON enables it.

In DOS 5, you can also prevent any single command from being echoed, by preceding it with an @ sign. Hence, the command @ECHO OFF suppresses echoing, and even prevents itself from being echoed.

You can also use ECHO to send a message to the screen, as in

```
@echo Welcome All!
```

Note that the @ sign may only be used in batch file commands, not in command line commands.

Pausing for a Keypress

The PAUSE command interrupts the batch file execution, and can also be used to display a message. PAUSE is often used as a prompt to the user to perform a task, such as "Insert a new disk in drive A, then press any key to continue...." It can also give the user a chance to terminate the macro, as shown here:

```
@echo Insert a new disk in drive A, then
@pause
```

To hide the "Press any key to continue..." message that PAUSE usually displays, you can send its output to the NUL device, as in this example:

```
@echo Press Ctrl+C to quit, or
@echo press any other key to continue...
@pause >NUL
```

Replaceable Parameters

In a single batch file, you can use up to ten replaceable parameters, named %0 through %9. These act as "placeholders" within the batch file, and get their values from the command line when the user runs the batch file. The %0 parameter is the command that executes the batch file, and %1 through %9 receive values from text to the right of the command.

For example, consider a simple batch file named C.BAT that contains only this one command:

```
copy %1 %2
```

If you run the C batch file by entering the command

```
c *.* a:
```

the command COPY %1 %2 is automatically changed to

```
copy *.* a:
```

before being executed. The blank spaces separating the parameters determine which one is assigned to %1, and which is assigned to %2. (In this case, %0 is assigned c, the first command in the line.)

Branching

GOTO command

The GOTO command sends control to any *label* in a batch file. The label must be the first entry on the line, and must start with a colon. For example, the command

```
GOTO alldone
```

passes control to a label that appears as

```
:alldone
```

at the beginning of a line in a batch file.

Decision Making

IF command

With the aid of the IF command, a batch file can also make rudimentary decisions about what to do next, based on a value. For example:

```
if "%1" == "Yes" goto doit
```

tells the batch file, "If the contents of the %1 parameter are the letters *Yes*, then send control to the line labeled DOIT." If, on the other hand, %1 does not contain *Yes*, the GOTO DOIT command is ignored, and execution resumes at the next line down.

Notice that double equal signs (==) are used for the comparison, and be aware that the comparisons are always case sensitive.

Check your DOS documentation for information on these three variations of IF:

IF EXIST *filename*	(Evaluates to "true" if *filename* exists)
IF ERRORLEVEL *number*	(Evaluates to "true" if error *number* occurs)
IF NOT	(Converts "if true" to "if false")

Looping

The FOR command lets a batch file repeat a command several times, each time with a different parameter. The basic syntax of FOR is

FOR command

```
FOR %%variable IN (value list) DO command
```

Thus if this loop

```
FOR %%x IN (C D E F) DO dir %%x:\%1 /s
```

is stored in a batch file named LOOKFOR.BAT, and you enter the command

```
lookfor myfile.txt
```

the batch file will search all the directories on hard disks C, D, E, and F for that file.

The DIR command in the loop shown above is executed four times, because there are four values listed (C, D, E, and F). Each time through the loop, the %%x parameter receives one of those four values, and substitutes it in the DIR command.

Batch Subprograms

A batch file can either run or call another batch file. To demonstrate the difference, consider two batch files named FIRST.BAT and SECOND.BAT. Suppose FIRST.BAT contains the command

```
second
```

When this command is executed in FIRST.BAT, control is passed to SECOND.BAT, whose commands are all executed. When SECOND.BAT is finished, control returns to the Shell or command prompt.

If, on the other hand, FIRST.BAT contains the command

```
call second
```

control is *temporarily* passed to SECOND.BAT. When all commands in SECOND.BAT have been executed, control is passed back to the next command in FIRST.BAT (rather than to the Shell or command prompt), and the rest of the commands in FIRST.BAT are executed. Thus the CALL command lets one batch file treat another batch file as a subroutine.

Again, if you are not a programmer, don't worry about learning the special programming language commands presented in this Step. Chances are you may never need to use them.

The next Step discusses the CONFIG.SYS and AUTOEXEC.BAT files, which help you configure and customize your system.

Configuring Your System

Whenever you turn on your computer, it searches the disk drives in order (first A, then B, then C, and so on) for a disk. It searches the first disk it finds for system tracks. If that disk does not have system tracks, the screen informs you that it cannot boot from a non-system disk, and the bootup procedure fails.

When the computer finds the system tracks, it loads DOS 5 from them. DOS then searches the root directory of that same disk for two files, named CONFIG.SYS and AUTOEXEC.BAT, and executes them. This Step discusses these two important files.

EDITING CONFIG.SYS AND AUTOEXEC.BAT

Keep in mind the following facts about CONFIG.SYS and AUTOEXEC.BAT:

- Before editing them, it's a good idea to make backup copies of your existing CONFIG.SYS and AUTOEXEC.BAT files. That way, if you corrupt them, you can simply copy healthy files back into your bootup drive and directory.

- You can edit both these files with any text editor, including the Editor described in Step 15. Don't use a word processing program unless it can create ASCII text files.

- Always save these files either on the root directory of drive C (C:\), or A:\ on your DOS Startup Disk if you do not have a hard disk. Otherwise DOS won't be able to find them during bootup.

- Any change you make to either CONFIG.SYS or AUTOEXEC.BAT is ignored until the next time you reboot. After changing either file, press Ctrl+Alt+Del to reboot and activate your changes. (If you've changed *only* AUTOEXEC.BAT, enter **autoexec** at the command prompt to reexecute just that file.)

THE CONFIG.SYS FILE

CONFIG.SYS ("configure system") is the first file that DOS executes during the booting-up process. This file sets up basic system parameters and loads the drivers for special devices, such as your mouse, hard disk cache, or a RAM disk. The most commonly used CONFIG.SYS commands are summarized in the sections that follow.

BREAK

Interrupt checking

The command BREAK=ON ensures that DOS responds quickly to an *interrupt* (that is, a Ctrl+Break or Ctrl+C keypress). A BREAK=OFF command tells DOS to check less frequently for an interrupt. This speeds overall performance slightly, but slows DOS's reaction to the interrupt keys.

BUFFERS

Disk buffers

Use BUFFERS to determine how much memory is set aside for disk buffering, in 512K units. A higher setting means faster disk access, but less memory is available for other jobs. In general, the following maximum buffer sizes are recommended:

Hard Disk Capacity	Buffer Size
Less than 40Mb	20
40Mb to 79Mb	30
80Mb to 119Mb	40
120Mb or more	50

DEVICE

The DEVICE command tells DOS to load the device driver (internal program) for a particular device. Always include the complete path to the driver, as DOS is not aware of any PATH setting while CONFIG.SYS is being executed.

For example, if you use a mouse, you might need a command like

```
device = c:\mouse1\mouse.sys
```

in your CONFIG.SYS file, so that the mouse software is loaded while the system is booting up.

FILES

FILES lets you determine the maximum number of files that can be open simultaneously, to a maximum of 255. The amount you need is actually determined by programs that can manage multiple files, such as spreadsheets and database management systems. You'll need to consult the manuals of such programs for specific information, but typically a setting of 30 to 40 is sufficient for most applications.

THE AUTOEXEC.BAT FILE

The AUTOEXEC.BAT file is executed after CONFIG.SYS and it can contain any valid DOS command (excluding the CONFIG.SYS commands). However, the commands most commonly included in this file are the ones that customize your system.

If you use the DOSSHELL command in your AUTOEXEC.BAT file to start the Shell, make sure that DOSSHELL is the *last* command in the file. If you execute DOSSHELL first, the Shell will "take over" your system before the remaining commands in AUTOEXEC.BAT are executed.

MODE

MODE is used primarily to configure parallel and serial printer ports. For example,

*Parallel
printers*

```
mode LPT1:80,6,p
```

configures the parallel port to print 80 columns across the page, 6 lines to the inch, and to keep trying the current print request until the printer accepts it. In most cases, you'll leave the first two parameters empty (by entering two commas) to use the printer's default settings. The p parameter, however, is usually specified. For example:

```
mode LPT1:,,p
```

*Serial
printers*

For serial printers, MODE is used to define the baud rate, parity, data bits, stop bits, and retry frequency, in that order (see your serial printer manual for specific settings). The most common setting for serial printers is

```
mode COM1:9600,n,8,1,p
```

If you have a serial printer, but no parallel printer, enter the preceding command (with appropriate parameters), followed by

```
mode LPT1 = COM1
```

This causes DOS to send printer output to the serial port, rather than the parallel port.

PATH

*Setting the
search path*

With PATH you tell DOS which drives and directories to search for program files (.BAT, .COM, and .EXE) if a requested program is not found in the current directory.

Directories are searched as listed (left to right), so you can maximize system performance by listing the most frequently accessed directories at the beginning of the PATH statement. For example, the following PATH statement tells DOS to search C:\WP51, then

C:\DOS, and then D:\DBASE (in that order) if a requested program cannot be found on the current directory. (You could include this command in your AUTOEXEC.BAT file.)

```
path c:\wp51;c:\dos;d:dbase
```

Note that the only blank space in the command is the one immediately after the command verb PATH.

Individual directory names must be separated by semicolons (;), and must not contain blank spaces (DOS interprets a blank space in the directory list as the end of the list!).

APPEND

APPEND is like PATH, except that it searches for files with extensions *other than* .BAT, .COM, and .EXE. Generally it is used only with older programs that cannot find their own overlay files if started from another directory.

Searching for non-program files

For example, suppose you have a favorite old text editor stored on C:\MYEDITOR, and that directory is in the PATH. Yet when you run that program from some other directory, the program fails and DOS tells you it cannot find necessary overlay files. You could avoid this error if you included the command

```
append c:\myeditor
```

in your AUTOEXEC.BAT file.

PROMPT

Use PROMPT to define the appearance of your command prompt. You can have it display any text, plus any combination of the symbols listed in Table 17.1.

Customizing the prompt

Command Parameter	Displays
$$	$ (dollar sign)
$b	¦ (split vertical bar)
$d	Current date
$e	Escape key symbol (ASCII 27)
$g	> (greater than)
$l (letter *l*)	< (less than)
$n	Current drive letter
$p	Current drive letter and path
$q	= (equals)
$t	Current time
$v	Current DOS version number

Table 17.1: Parameters Used with PROMPT

Other PROMPT options

In addition to the symbols shown in the table, you can use $_ to break the prompt into two lines (starting at the symbol), and $h to backspace and erase characters in the prompt.

For example, the default PROMPT setting

```
prompt $p$g
```

displays the familiar command prompt, with the current drive and directory followed by a greater-than sign (>). This command

```
prompt $v$_Yes? $g
```

replaces the default prompt with

```
MS-DOS Version 5.0
Yes? >_
```

Some additional commands that you can use in CONFIG.SYS and AUTOEXEC.BAT to fine-tune your system are covered in Step 18.

Improving Performance

There are two ways in which DOS can help you optimize your system's performance: by using memory efficiently, and by maximizing the speed of your hard disk.

ABOUT MEMORY

Four types of memory are used in modern computers:

- *Conventional memory* ("standard" RAM) is up to 640K on most systems.

- *Reserved memory* (also called "upper memory") is the 384K of memory above conventional memory that is typically used to control the monitor, hard disk, and other devices.

- *Extended memory* (also called XMS) is memory above 640K RAM. Requires a device driver in order to be used by programs.

- *Expanded memory* (also called EMS) is memory above 640K that conforms to the Lotus-Intel-Microsoft (LIM) standard. Requires a device driver (called an *expanded memory manager*).

A typical 640K computer has 640K conventional memory, followed by 384K reserved memory—for a total of 1Mb. Extended or expanded memory begins at the first byte after that first 1Mb.

*Checking
current
memory*

MANAGING MEMORY

To see how much and what kind of memory is currently available on your system, enter the command

mem

at the command prompt.

Even if MEM does not report it, your system probably has 384K of reserved memory.

For a more detailed listing of the current status of your system's memory, you can use these optional switches with MEM:

*MEM
switches*

/classify (or /c) displays the names and sizes of programs in conventional memory and upper memory (if any), as well as the remaining available memory.

/program (or /p) displays the names of programs currently in memory, and their locations in hexadecimal.

/debug (or /d) displays programs, internal drivers, and other information about memory.

The sections that follow discuss basic techniques for configuring your system's memory.

All of the examples that follow are for a system with its DOS device drivers stored on the C:\DOS directory, as in a normal hard disk installation. If you've stored these files on a different drive and/or directory, you'll need to make the appropriate changes to the c:\dos parameter in each command example.

Using HIMEM.SYS

*Extended
memory*

HIMEM is a device driver that manages your system's extended memory, and can be used by many modern programs, including Windows 3 and its family of applications. Place the following command in your CONFIG.SYS file to install HIMEM.SYS:

```
device = c:\dos\himem.sys
```

Storing DOS in Extended Memory

Normally DOS and its internal commands are loaded into a portion of conventional memory when you start your computer. This arrangement bars other programs from using that memory. However, if your computer has extended memory (XMS), you can instead load DOS into the first 64K of XMS. This memory area, called the *high memory area* (HMA), is rarely used by other programs, so it's an ideal place to store DOS.

Conserving conventional memory

To load DOS into the HMA, add this command to your CONFIG.SYS file, anywhere *below* the command that loads HIMEM.SYS:

```
dos = high
```

This technique saves you about 54K of conventional memory.

Using Expanded Memory

Every expanded memory (EMS) board requires its own driver. DOS offers nothing to take advantage of expanded memory on 286 and lower model computers. However, the EMM386 utility that comes with DOS 5 can *emulate* expanded memory, using extended (XMS) memory, if you have a 386 or 486 machine. This lets you run programs that require EMS, without installing an EMS board.

386 and 486 machines

You can specify how much extended memory to allocate to expanded memory, up to the full amount of your extended memory. For example, to install the EMM386 utility and use one megabyte of extended memory to emulate expanded memory, you would add this command to your CONFIG.SYS file:

```
device = c:\dos\emm386.exe 1024
```

Make sure that the line that installs HIMEM.SYS *precedes* the line that installs EMM386 in your CONFIG.SYS file. Also, if you use EMM386, disable any other expanded memory managers.

Accessing Reserved Memory

*Upper
memory
blocks*

DOS allocates some portions of reserved memory to devices, such as your hard disk controller and video monitor. Any remaining unused reserved memory can be set aside as *upper memory blocks* (abbreviated UMB), which you can use to store device drivers and TSR (terminate-and-stay-resident) programs. You need to use a combination of the HIMEM device drive, the DOS= command, the EMM386 utility to set things up. Then you can use the DE-VICEHIGH command and LOADHIGH commands to store device drivers and programs in upper, rather than conventional, memory.

The command to install HIMEM.SYS must be the first in the series in CONFIG.SYS. Next, add the command DOS = UMB to tell DOS to maintain a link between conventional and reserved memory. You can combine umb with high if you wish, like this:

```
dos = high, umb
```

so that DOS itself it still loaded into high memory rather than conventional memory.

Next, you need to activate EMM386 with one of the following command options:

NOEMS   Activates reserved memory (UMBs) only; does not support programs that require expanded memory.

RAM   Activates reserved memory (UMBs), and also lets programs that require EMS memory to run (one block of reserved memory is used as an EMS page frame).

For example, if you want to be able to load device drivers and TSR's in reserved memory, and don't need to be concerned about expanded memory (the most likely scenario), you would want to put this series of commands in CONFIG.SYS:

```
device=c:\dos\himem.sys
dos=high,umb
device=c:\dos\emm386.exe noems
```

Optionally, you could use the next series of commands to activate reserved memory, and also use 1MB (1024K) of extended memory to emulate expanded memory:

```
device=c:\dos\himem.sys
dos=high,umb
device=c:\dos\emm386.exe 1024 ram
```

Next, to load a device driver into UMBs, use the DEVICEHIGH= command instead of DEVICE=, *beneath* all three command lines listed above. For example, to load your mouse driver (assuming you normally load it with a DEVICE= command) into an upper memory block rather than conventional memory, change the device=c:\mouse\mouse.sys command to

Loading device drivers

```
devicehigh=c:\mouse\mouse.sys
```

To load a TSR program into upper memory blocks, use the LOADHIGH command at the command prompt or in your AUTOEXEC.BAT file (*not* in CONFIG.SYS). For example, if you want to load the resident portion of the DOS PRINT program (PRINT.EXE) into upper memory blocks, and that program is stored on the C:\DOS directory, include this command in your AUTOEXEC.BAT file:

Loading TSR programs

```
loadhigh c:\dos\print.exe /d:lpt1
```

If there is not sufficient memory for your TSRs in the UMBs, DOS loads the programs into conventional memory, *without* indicating that it did so. You'll need to use the MEM /c command to inspect memory and verify the command's success. (See "System Optimization" in Appendix A.)

MAXIMIZING HARD DISK PERFORMANCE

Aside from printing, disk accessing is generally the slowest operation on any computer. *Disk caching,* which uses memory to keep track of the frequently used files and directories, can help you optimize disk peformance.

Using SMARTDrive

SMARTDrive is a general-purpose disk caching program that operates in either extended or expanded memory. This utility must be installed via your CONFIG.SYS file, using the syntax

```
device = [path]smartdrv.sys[init][min][/a]
```

where *init* is the initial size of the cache, ranging from 128K to 8192K; 256K is the default if you omit this parameter. The *min* option specifies the minimum size to which the cache may be reduced by any application; zero is the default if you omit this parameter. The /a switch specifies expanded, rather than extended memory. If the /a switch is omitted, SMARTDrive is stored in extended memory.

Some programs create their own caches. You should omit the *min* parameter in the DEVICE= command for these programs, so that they reduce the SMARTDrive cache to zero K. This prevents a "cache within a cache," which may slow system performance.

The following command installs SMARTDrive in extended memory with the default settings:

```
device = c:\dos\smartdriv.sys
```

To install SMARTDrive in expanded memory, with an initial cache size of one megabyte, and a minimum cache size of 512K, enter

```
device = c:\dos\smartdrv.sys 1024 512 /a
```

In your CONFIG.SYS file, the command to install SMARTDrive must be listed *after* the command that installs HIMEM.SYS, and, if you use the /a switch, *after* EMM386.SYS. Never use DEVICEHIGH= to load SMARTDrive—you might lose data.

Using Fastopen

The Fastopen program keeps track of the names and locations of frequently used files, to speed up disk accessing. Unlike the general-purpose SMARTDrive, Fastopen is useful only with programs that open and close files frequently, such as database management systems and compilers.

The general syntax of the FASTOPEN installation command is

```
fastopen drive: [=n] [...] [/x]
```

where *drive* is the disk drive with which you want to activate Fastopen; *n* is the number of file names to track (from 10 to 999); [...] indicates additional drives for Fastopen; and /x uses expanded memory rather than conventional memory.

If you want to use the /x switch with Fastopen to use expanded rather than conventional memory, make sure that your expanded memory manager (or EMM386) is installed before you use Fastopen. Fastopen cannot use extended memory.

With the following command entered either at the command prompt or in AUTOEXEC.BAT, DOS 5 will track 40 file names on drives D and E:

```
fastopen d:=40 e:=40
```

You can install Fastopen through your CONFIG.SYS file using the INSTALL command, as in this example:

```
install = c:\dos\fastopen.exe c:=100
```

Each file name you track requires 48 bytes of memory. Thus, Fastopen installed with the foregoing command will use 4800 bytes of conventional memory.

CREATING A RAM DISK

A RAM disk is a portion of memory configured to appear as a disk drive to DOS. Because it's a *virtual* drive with no moving parts, a RAM disk is hundreds of times faster than a "real" disk. On the other hand, because it's stored in memory, everything on it is lost the moment you turn off the computer. Because of this volatility, one of the best uses for a RAM disk is for storing temporary files created by other programs.

To create a RAM disk, activate the RAMDRIVE.SYS device driver from your CONFIG.SYS file. You can specify a size (in kilobytes), and either extended memory (/e) or expanded memory (/a). If you use neither switch, RAMDRIVE uses conventional memory.

For example, this CONFIG.SYS file command creates a 360K RAM disk in extended memory:

```
device = c:\dos\ramdrive.sys 360 /e
```

If you want to use extended memory (/e) for the RAM disk, the HIMEM.SYS must be installed first (in CONFIG.SYS). If you want to use expanded memory (/a), the expanded memory manager must be installed first (in CONFIG.SYS).

If you use DEVICEHIGH= to load a RAM disk, DOS will correctly load *only* the RAM disk driver into reserved memory (saving about 1200 bytes of conventional memory). The RAM disk itself still (correctly) uses extended, expanded, or conventional memory, as specified by the /e, /a, or lack of a switch.

DOS automatically assigns the next available drive name to the RAM disk (you'll see it listed as a drive in the Shell). For example, consider a RAM disk named H. To use the H drive for temporary files, first create a subdirectory on it, and set the TEMP environmental variable to that subdirectory. Do so with commands in AUTOEXEC.BAT not CONFIG.SYS, as in this example:

```
md h:\temps
set temp = h:\temps
```

Programs that check for the TEMP variable will thus use the \temps directory or the RAM disk for temporary files.

Unerasing and Unformatting

DOS 5 can help you undo your mistakes—you can "unerase" accidentally erased files, and "unformat" accidentally reformatted floppy and hard disks to regain your original files. To aid in the recovery, DOS can use either, or both of the following:

- *Mirror files,* which keep track of disk format and deleted file information

- Information in the disk's root directory and *file allocation table* (FAT)

The mirror files are the most reliable recovery tool, but their use requires that you run the MIRROR program first.

RUNNING MIRROR

The MIRROR program is a TSR program that creates and keeps track of the files that DOS 5 can use in unformatting and undeleting files. Its basic syntax is

```
MIRROR [drive:[ ...]] [/1] [/Tdrive[-entries]
  [...]]
```

MIRROR syntax

Here are the MIRROR parameter definitions.

drive: and [...] list the hard disk (not floppy disk) drives for which you want MIRROR to maintain format information files. The information, used in unformatting, is stored in a file named MIRROR.FIL on the root directory of the drive.

/tdrive: indicates the drives for which you want MIRROR to maintain *delete-tracking files,* used in undeleting files. There is a hidden file for each drive you specify, called PCTRACKR.DEL, stored on the root directory of the disk being tracked.

-entries indicates how many deleted files you want to track, from 1 to 999. If you omit this option, a default number of entries is used, based on disk size, as listed in Table 19.1. The Table also shows the resulting file size.

/1 limits a disk to one copy of the MIRROR.FIL file, and therefore only one generation of unformatting. If you omit this option, and you create a new MIRROR.FIL on a disk that already has one, the existing file is renamed to MIRROR.BAK before the new MIRROR.FIL file is created.

Tracking file defaults

Disk Size	Entries	File Size
360K	25	5K
720Kd	50	9K
1.2Mb	75	14K
1.44Mb	75	15K
20Mb	101	18K
32Mb	202	36K
Over 32Mb	303	55K

Table 19.1: Default Size of Delete-Tracking Files

You can run the MIRROR program at any time directly from the command prompt. However, it makes more sense to install MIRROR from your AUTOEXEC.BAT file, to be sure that MIRROR's information is available when you need it.

Here are some other examples of valid MIRROR commands.

```
mirror
```

saves a copy of the FAT and root directory for the current drive, in MIRROR.FIL on the root directory.

```
mirror c: /ta /tb /tc
```

creates a mirror file for unformatting hard disk drive C, and installs delete-tracking files for drives A, B, and C.

```
mirror c: d: e: /tc-200 /td-200
```

creates mirror files for drives C, D, and E, and also tracks up to 200 files names for undeleting on drives C and D.

The following two additional MIRROR command switches must be used alone on the command line:

/u disables the delete-tracking capability (available only if MIRROR was the last TSR loaded).

Disabling MIRROR

/partn saves information about how the disk is partitioned to a floppy disk.

Here are examples. The command

```
mirror /partn
```

saves a copy of the hard disk partition table, in a file named PARTNSAV.FIL on the floppy disk in drive A. Note that you cannot rebuild a partition table without first running MIRROR with /partn, as explained later in this Step. (Step 20, also, discusses disk partitions.)

Always save the PARTNSAV.FIL file on a floppy—never on the hard disk.

The command

```
mirror /u
```

disables all delete-tracking files and removes the resident portion of MIRROR from memory. If other TSRs have been loaded since MIRROR, these must be removed from memory before you use the /u switch.

UNDELETING FILES

When you delete a file using the Delete option on File menu, or the ERASE or DEL command, DOS 5 simply changes the first character of the deleted file's name to a special character that makes the file "invisible." Later, when you save other files, DOS will overwrite the space occupied by the "invisible" file. You can, however, undelete the file and regain all of its contents, if you do this before DOS overwrites the file.

Avoid using the UNDELETE command with the Windows LOAD= command or Shift+Enter keys, or when other programs are running in the Task Swapper.

Using
UNDELETE

To undelete files, use the UNDELETE command. There are two ways to do so. From the Shell,

1. Use the drives area and Directory Tree to get to the drive and directory from which you want to undelete files.

2. Select Disk Utilities from the Main program group.

3. Select Undelete.

4. You can press Backspace and type new parameters and/or switches for the command; or do nothing to use the default /list switch (described later).

5. Select OK or press Enter to execute UNDELETE in the text box.

At the DOS command prompt,

1. Switch to the drive and directory on which you want to un-delete files. For example, to switch to C:\DOS, type

    ```
    c:
    cd\dos
    ```

    Be sure to press Enter after typing each command.

2. Type **UNDELETE** at the prompt, using any of the param-eters or switches described below.

Keep in mind that, like everything else in DOS, it doesn't really matter whether you initiate the UNDELETE command from the Shell or the command prompt—it's still the same command.

For example, the command

```
UNDELETE Rescue.me
```

whether executed from the Shell or command prompt, attempts to undelete a file named Rescue.me from the current directory. The command

```
UNDELETE *.bat
```

attempts to undelete deleted files that have the .BAT extension on the current directory. The command

```
UNDELETE
```

gives you a chance to undelete every deleted file on the current directory, but individually asks for permission before each undeletion.

Exactly *how* UNDELETE goes about its job depends on whether or not MIRROR has been installed, as explained next.

Undeleting with MIRROR Tracking

When you enter the UNDELETE command, DOS first attempts to locate the delete-tracking file (PCTRACKR.DEL). If it finds that file, you'll see information about the tracking file and the number of recoverable files. You'll also see the name, size, creation date and time, and deletion date and time for the first recoverable file.

- If the file is recoverable, you'll see the message "Do you want to recover this file? (Y/N)" beneath the file name, as shown below. Type **Y** for yes, or **N** for No.

```
Using the Delete Tracking file.
TEST BAT   89   4/15/91   1:00 ...A   Deleted
    4/19/91   11:55
```

> All of the clusters for this file are
> available.
> Do you want to recover this file? (Y/N)

- If the file is not recoverable, you'll see a message to this effect, and a prompt to press any key to continue.

- If you've opted to undelete more than one file, you'll see information and options for those files, one at a time.

Because PCTRACKR.DEL is a hidden file, it's only visible in the Files List if Display Hidden/System Files is checked in the File Display Options dialog box (accessible via the Shell's Options menu), or when you're using the /as switch with the DIR command.

Undeleting without MIRROR Tracking

If MIRROR was not active when you deleted a file, your UN-DELETE command displays the names of deleted files, with a question mark (?) as the first character of each file name. If the file is recoverable, you're asked if you want to undelete a file. If you type Y for Yes, you're prompted to type the correct first letter of the file name, to replace the ?.

If MIRROR tracking is not active, and the UNDELETE command alone does not offer the opportunity to recover your file, try using the /dos switch to view the names of deleted files not listed in the PCTRACKR.DEL file (e.g. UNDELETE C:\MYFILES*.* /DOS).

Optional UNDELETE Switches

Here are some switches you can use with UNDELETE.

UNDELETE
switches

/list lists the files that can be recovered (the default switch when run from the Shell).

/dt limits recovery to files listed in PCTRACKR.DEL.

/dos limits recovery to deleted files not in PCTRACKR.DEL.

/all undeletes all recoverable files without asking for permission first. The first character of deleted files not listed in PCTRACKR.DEL is replaced by a # character. However, if the # results in a duplicate file name, DOS inserts one of the following characters (in the order shown here)—&–0123456789— until the file name is not a duplicate of an existing file name. If the resulting file name is still a duplicate, the letters A through Z are used until a unique file name exists.

The /dt, /dos, and /all switches are mutually exclusive—you can only use one of them in your UNDELETE command. If you don't use any of them, UNDELETE works as though you entered /all, except that it asks for permission before recovering each file.

If you delete a directory, you cannot UNDELETE files on that directory. Also, because DOS eventually reclaims the space used by deleted files, you should undelete as soon as you realize your mistake.

USING UNFORMAT

The UNFORMAT command lets you unformat (rebuild) an accidentally reformatted hard or floppy disk, thereby recovering any files that were lost during the accidental reformat. As with undeleting, the sooner you realize and correct the mistake, the better your chances of recovering the lost files.

Be aware that, once you format your hard disk, there is almost never a need to reformat it. To play it safe, always limit your formatting activities to the floppy drives (A: and B:), unless you know *exactly* what you're doing. Furthermore, never "experiment" with UNFORMAT, unless you do so with unimportant floppy disks.

How DOS 5 Formatting Works

It's easiest to understand unformatting if you first understand the three types of formatting that DOS 5 offers:

Quick Format: This technique (using the Quick Format option from the Disk Utilities program group, or FORMAT with the /Q switch at the command prompt) attempts to reformat a previously formatted disk very quickly. If the disk has never been formatted, this technique defaults to the Unconditional Format technique explained below.

Format: Reformats a formatted disk, but saves UNFORMAT information in case you change your mind and want to unformat later. This type of format is performed by the Format option in the Disk Utilities program group, or the FORMAT command at the prompt with no switches.

Unconditional Format: Does not save any UNFORMAT information on the disk. This is the default when formatting a disk that has never been formatted (since there is no UNFORMAT information to save anyway), or if you use the optional /U switch with the FORMAT command at the command prompt.

In general, Quick Format provides the best method of formatting floppies, since it saves a great deal of time when reformatting a previously formatted floppy. Also, it allows unformatting, and performs the correct unconditional type of format if the disk has never before been formatted.

Unformatting a Disk

To unformat an accidentally reformatted disk,

1. If you are at the Shell, press F3 to get to the command prompt.

2. Type **UNFORMAT** followed by a space and the letter of the drive that contains the disk you want to unformat; for example, type **UNFORMAT A:** or **UNFORMAT B:**. Then press Enter.

3. As prompted, insert the disk to be unformatted into the appropriate drive (A: or B:) and press Enter.

You will first see warnings reminding you that UNFORMAT should *only* be used to unformat a disk that has accidentally been reformatted, and then additional instructions depending on the situation, as described in the sections that follow. You'll also be reminded in the warning messages that, if you saved any files on this disk since it was accidentally reformatted, those files will be destroyed during the unformat procedure. If necessary, copy these files to another disk before proceeding with UNFORMAT.

Unformatting with Valid Mirror File

If the disk to be unformatted contains a valid mirror file (MIRROR.FIL) for unformatting, you will see a message indicating this, along with a prompt asking if you are *sure* you want to update the SYSTEM area. If you are simply unformatting an accidentally unformatted floppy disk, type **Y** for Yes.

When the unformat is complete, you'll see a message that the SYSTEM area has been rebuilt, and that you may need to reboot. Unless you have unformatted your boot drive (usually C:), you can ignore the message about rebooting. Enter **DIR A:** or **DIR B:** to view the names of recovered files.

Unformatting without a Mirror File

DOS will tell you if it cannot locate a mirror (UNFORMAT information) file on the disk you are attempting to unformat, and will ask if you want DOS to search the hard disk for that file. Without a mirror file, chances are that the floppy disk cannot be unformatted, but answer Yes just to double-check. The screen will then display information and options telling you how DOS will attempt to unformat the disk. Read the messages carefully—you'll see information about what's safe, and what's not safe, given the current situation.

Saving Time

Unformatting a disk can be a time-consuming process, particularly if you force DOS to make most of the decisions. Here are several optional switches that you can use with UNFORMAT to speed things along. (The examples provided with each switch assume that you are unformatting the disk in drive A. If you are unformatting a disk in another drive, substitute that drive name in each example.)

/j tells DOS to "just check" the status of the mirror file before attempting to unformat. Example: **UNFORMAT A: /j.** If this test fails, answer No to the prompt, and try the /test switch.

/test tells DOS to test the results of an UNFORMAT request when no mirror file is available. This test takes a while, but gives you a clue as to what the result will be if you actually proceed with the /L switch. Example: **UNFORMAT A: /test.**

/L (That's the letter *L*, for "let it happen.") If the results of the /test switch encourage you to proceed with UNFORMAT without the aid of the mirror file, you can proceed by using the /L switch. Example: **UNFORMAT A: /L.**

/P sends unformat information to the printer. Example: **UNFORMAT A: /j /p.**

As complicated as all of this sounds, keep in mind that DOS 5 wants to make recovery simple. Unformatting is really just an attempt at helping you recover from mistakes that you probably could have avoided in the first place. So, even though DOS 5 offers these handy recovery methods, the old "think before you format" approach that was *enforced* by earlier versions of DOS still reigns supreme in DOS 5.

Rebuilding the Disk Partitions

To rebuild the disk partition table, use UNFORMAT without a drive parameter, and with the /partn switch.

```
unformat /partn
```

You'll be prompted to insert the disk that contains the PARTNSAV.FIL file, which you must have previously created with the MIRROR /partn command. Insert the disk, and then enter the name of the drive in which you inserted that disk (e.g. A). Follow the remaining instructions that appear on the screen.

After the partition table is recovered, use UNFORMAT with the switches described earlier to test and rebuild each partition as a separate drive.

Partitioning
Your Hard Disk

If you plan to use DOS 5 and one or more additional operating systems (such as XENIX) on your computer, you need to *partition* your hard disk. Even if you do plan to use only DOS, you might still want to partition your hard disk into several separate *logical drives,* each with its own letter name (C, D, E, and so forth).

IMPORTANT WARNING

When you buy a new computer with a hard disk, there's a good chance that the manufacturer or dealer has already partitioned the hard disk for you, so you may never need to partition it yourself. If you do decide to partition (or repartition) your hard disk, keep in mind these very important points:

- If the hard disk has already been partitioned by, and is driven by a third-party program manufacturer—such as Disk Manager (DMDRVR.BIN), SpeedStor (SSTOR.SYS or HARDRIVE.SYS), VFeature Deluxe (FIXT_DRV.SYS), HP MultiVol (MULTIVOL.SYS) or HP Volume Expansion (HARDRIVE.SYS)—refer to the DOS 5 documentation before repartitioning with the FDISK command described in this Step.

- *Never* attempt to repartition a hard disk unless you've backed it up completely, with a backup system that you understand thoroughly and can use to recover from a major loss of important files.

TYPES OF PARTITIONS

DOS 5 allows you to create several types of partitions.

- The *primary DOS partition* is the one that stores the DOS 5 system tracks, the COMMAND.COM file, and other DOS files.

- The *extended DOS partition* is also used by DOS 5, but is considered to be one or more separate drives. Extended partitions are optional.

- A *non-DOS partition* is one used by an operating system other than DOS 5.

- The *active partition* is a primary partition that holds an operating system, and is used for booting up when you turn on the computer.

Unlike earlier versions, DOS 5 lets you create partitions that are larger than 32Mb, *without* having to use the SHARE utility. A hard disk can contain a maximum of four partitions.

USING FDISK

The FDISK utility is used to partition a new disk, or re-partition an existing disk. To run FDISK, enter the command

```
fdisk
```

at the command prompt. The FDISK main menu presents the following options:

```
Current fixed disk drive: 1

...

1. Create DOS partitions or Logical DOS Drive
2. Set active partition
3. Delete DOS partition or Logical DOS Drive
```

4. Display partition information
...
Press **Esc** to exit FDISK

Creating/deleting partitions or logical drives (options 1 and 3 from the menu) on a disk that already contains files causes a substantial loss of files that cannot be recovered. See "Deleting Drives and Partitions" later in this Step.

To select an option from the FDISK main menu, type the option number and press Enter. Press Esc to exit FDISK.

Selecting FDISK options

The Current Drive

Physical hard disk drives on your system are numbered 1, 2, and so forth. The current fixed disk (the one on which you started FDISK) is shown near the top of the FDISK main menu screen. Note that physical fixed drives are not the same as logical drives. For example, if you have a 130Mb hard disk logically divided into drives C through G, you still have only one physical drive, numbered 1.

Physical vs. logical

If you do have several physical drives, you can select a different hard drive to work with from the top of the menu screen.

Displaying Current Partition Information

To review the current partition information for your hard disk, select option 4. The resulting display shows the

- Letter name of each partition (or none, if the partition is divided into logical drives)

- Partition status (where A means "Active")

- Partition type (for example, PRI DOS for Primary DOS, and EXT DOS for Extended DOS)

- Size of the partition in megabytes

- Percentage of total capacity used by the partition

If a partition contains logical drives, you'll see a message indicating this. You can press Enter to view information about the logical drives. It will show you the name, volume label (if any), size, and percent of overall storage used by each logical drive in the partition. Press Esc after viewing this information, to return to the FDISK main menu.

CREATING A PRIMARY DOS PARTITION

If you want your hard disk to start DOS, the disk must have a primary DOS partition.

Obviously, if you can already start DOS from your hard disk, it already has a primary DOS partition, so you don't need to create a new one. However, should you need to change the size of your primary DOS partition, you'll first have to delete the existing primary and extended partitions (if any), and all logical drives— which permanently deletes *every* file on your hard disk!

After changing the primary DOS partition, you'll also need to boot up from a floppy. You should therefore create (and test) a bootable floppy that contains a copy of COMMAND.COM and FORMAT.COM, *before* you repartition the hard disk.

To create a new primary DOS partition,

1. Select option 1 from the FDISK main menu.

2. Select Create Primary DOS Partition.

3. You'll see a message asking if you want to use the maximum size for this partition, and also make it the active partition.

   To use the default size (100%), and to make this the primary partition, press Enter to answer Yes.

   If you don't want to use your entire disk as the primary DOS partition, answer No. Then indicate the number of megabytes (or the percent of overall capacity, followed by a % sign) that you want to allocate to the primary DOS partition.

4. Press Esc to leave FDISK, until you see the message "System will now restart."

5. When prompted, insert a system disk (the bootable floppy) into drive A, and follow the directions on the screen.

You'll need to format the new primary DOS partition, and copy the system tracks to it. For the C drive, for instance, you would enter the command

Formatting the primary partition

```
format c: /s
```

Finally, you can install DOS 5 on the new partition, as described in Step 1 of this book.

CREATING AN EXTENDED PARTITION

If you did not allocate 100% of your disk space to your primary DOS partition, you can create an extended partition, which in turn can be subdivided into smaller logical drives.

1. Select option 1 from the FDISK main menu.

2. Select Create Extended DOS partition.

3. You'll see the total number of unpartitioned bytes (if any) available for the partition. Press Enter to accept the default value; or enter the number of megabytes (or percentage of available space, followed by a % sign) to allocate to the extended partition.

4. You'll next be prompted to create logical drives. Type the volume label (if any) and number of megabytes (or percentage of space, followed by a % sign) to allocate to each logical drive. Continue doing so until you've used up all the available space, or have created all the logical drives you want.

Creating logical drives

5. Press Esc until you exit FDISK.

Now you need to format each logical drive that you created. For example, to format logical drive D, enter the command

Formatting logical drives

```
format d:
```

STEP 20

DELETING DRIVES AND PARTITIONS

You cannot change the size of a partition, or its logical drives. Instead, you need to delete the entire existing partition, and then re-create it.

When you delete a partition, *all* files in *every* logical drive within that partition are irrevocably deleted. Therefore, before you delete a partition, make sure you have copies of all files for that partition on floppies, or on some other partition that you will not be deleting (but *not* on another logical drive on the same partition!).

To delete a logical drive or partition,

1. Select option 3 from the FDISK main menu.

2. Select the type of partition (or logical drive) that you want to delete.

3. Follow instructions on the screen, and *heed all warnings* about files that will be lost.

4. When you're finished, press Esc until you get to the command prompt or restart message.

Note: If you delete the primary DOS 5 partition, you will have to boot up from a floppy disk.

CREATING NON-DOS PARTITIONS

Other operating systems

A non-DOS partition is an area of the hard disk used by an operating system other than DOS 5. DOS 5 cannot create non-DOS partitions. You'll need to consult the documentation for the other system to determine how to create a partition for it.

OS/2 PM is one exception to this rule. Since this system is downwardly compatible with DOS 5, OS/2 can be stored in a regular directory of any DOS drive.

CHANGING THE ACTIVE PARTITION

When you use several operating systems on your computer, you determine the currently operating system by making its partition the *active partition*.

Activating another system

To change the active partition, select option 2 from the FDISK main menu. From the next screen that appears, select the active partition. (Only a primary partition can be used as the active partition.)

Again, OS/2 PM is the exception. OS/2's DUALBOOT program lets you determine whether DOS 5, or OS/2, is in control. Or you can choose one or the other during bootup.

A

active partitions, 148, 153
altered files, backing up, 53
APPEND command, 127
appending output, 93–94, 102
archive files, 63
associating files, 33–35
asterisks (*), 25, 27
at sign (@) in batch files, 119
attributes, file, 63–64
AUTOEXEC.BAT file,
     125–128

B

background color, 83
background printing, 94–95
backing up hard disks, 3–4,
     51–53, 147
Bad command or file name
     message, 32–33
.BAT (batch) files, 31, 33, 72,
     101–102, 104–106, 117–122
blocking text, 111
bootable disks, 44–46
branches, directory tree, 24–26
branching in batch files, 120
BREAK command, 124
BUFFERS command for
     files, 124
buffers for commands, 99–100
buttons, dialog box, 15

C

caches, disk, 133–134
CALL command, 72, 122
canceling
  commands, 88
  dialog box changes, 15–16
  pull-down menus, 11–12
case sensitivity, 87, 112, 114,
     121
check boxes, 15
clicking the mouse, 10
collapsing directory trees,
     26–27
colors, 79–84, 110–111
.COM files, 31, 33
COM1 device, 93
COMMAND.COM file, 45–46
commands
  buffer for, 99–100
  canceling, 88
  command prompt for, 85–87
  editing, 88–89, 100–101
  external, 89–92
  help for, 19–21, 87–88
  internal, 33, 45, 89–90
  menu, 10–12
  multiple, 101–102
  for programs, 72–73
  reusing, 100–101
  in Shell, 92
comments in batch files, 118
COMP command, 48

help from, 20–21
messages with batch files,
    118–119
minus sign (–) in directory
    trees, 24, 26
MIRROR program, 137–139,
    141–142, 145
MODE command, 126
modified files, backing up, 53
MORE command, 95
mouse
  confirmation for, 59–61
  dragging, 10, 61–62, 78
  starting programs with, 38–39
mouse pointer, 9–10
moving
  within dialog boxes, 14
  files, 61–62, 78
  text, 111–112
MSDOS.SYS file, 45
multiple commands, 101–102
multiple files, selecting, 55–57
multiple programs, running,
    36–38

N

names
  for color schemes, 83
  for directories, 49–50
  for disks and disk drives, 1, 43
  for files, 1, 62, 116
  for macros, 102–103, 105
  for program groups, 68–69
  sorting files by, 28, 97

navigating file system, 23–29
non-DOS partitions, 148, 152
Non-system disk or disk error
    message, 45
NOT batch file condition, 121
NUL device, 93

O

online help for EDIT, 108
OS/2 operating systems, parti-
    tions for, 152–153
output, redirection of, 93–94,
    102

P

parallel printers, 126
parameters
  for batch files, 72–73, 102,
    119–120
  for commands, 87
  for macros, 103, 105–106
partial backups, 53
partitions, disk
  creating, 147–153
  rebuilding, 146
  saving tables for, 139
PARTNSAV.FIL file, 139, 146
passwords for program groups,
    68, 74
PATH command and paths, 2,
    33, 58, 72, 126–127
PAUSE command in batch
    files, 119

pausing at program termination, 74
PCTRACKR.DEL file, 138, 141–143
performance
  of hard disks, 133–135
  and memory, 129–133, 135–136
peripheral devices, command for, 125
physical hard disks, 149
piping, 93, 95–97, 102
plus sign (+) in directory trees, 24–25
Preview command, 79
primary DOS partitions, 148, 150–151
PRINT command, 94–95
printers, 94, 126
printing, 93–95, 115
PRN device, 93
Program/File Lists, 77
programming batch files, 118
programs and Program List window
  associating files with, 33–35
  groups of, 67–71
  memory for, 130
  properties of, 71–76
  running, 31–39
PROMPT command, 127–128
properties of programs, 71–76
protecting files, 63
PrtSc key, 94
pull-down menus, 10–13

Q

question marks (?), 27, 87, 89
Quick Format, 43–44, 143–144

R

radio buttons, 15
RAM (random-access memory). *See* memory
RAM disks and RAMDRIVE.SYS file, 135–136
read-only files, 63
recovering
  from abnormal failures, 38
  deleted files, 137–146
redirection, 93–94, 102
reformatting hard disks, 42
REM command, 118
renaming
  directories, 50
  files, 62
repeating commands, 88–89
replaceable parameters, 72–73, 102, 119–120
replacing
  files, 59–60
  text, 113–114
reserved memory, 129–130, 132–133
restoring backup files, 53–54
reverse order
  for displaying files, 28, 97
  for sorting text, 96

root directory, 24, 123
Run command, 32, 92
running
    batch files, 118
    programs, 31–39

S

saving
    dialog box text, 14–16
    with EDIT, 115–116
    macros, 104–105
    screen dumps, 94
    screen editor. *See* EDIT
scroll bars, 9, 16–19
scrolling with EDIT, 110
searching
    for files, 2, 33, 58, 72,
        126–127
    macro for, 103
    for text, 95–96
selecting
    directories, 24
    disk drives, 23, 41
    files, 55–58
    from lists, 16–18
    views, 77–78
serial printers, 126
SETUP file, 4
Shell
    accessing, 7–8
    appearance of text and graph-
        ics in, 78–79
    areas of, 8–9

colors for, 79–84
entering commands in, 92
exiting from, 85–86
views with, 77–78
shortcut keys, 73–76
Show Information window,
    64–65
size of files
    for comparing, 48
    delete-tracking, 138
    sorting by, 28, 97
slaving printers, 94
SMARTDrive, 134
sorting
    files names, 28, 97
    text, 96–97
source disks, 47
special characters, 105, 115
starting
    directory for, 73
    DOS, 5–6
    EDIT, 107–108
    programs, 31–39
status line, 9
subdirectories. *See* directories
subprograms in batch files, 122
suppressing output, 93
swapping programs, 36–38, 76
switches, command, 87
symbols, menu, 12
SYS command, 46
SYSTEM area and
    unformatting, 145
system files and tracks, 29,
    44–46, 63

T

target disks, 47
Task Swapper, 36–38, 76, 85
text, 9, 75
  appearance of, 78–79
  in dialog boxes, 14
  editing, 111–112
  replacing, 113–114
  searching for, 95–96, 112–114
  sorting, 96–97
title bar, 8
titles
  for color schemes, 83
  for program groups, 68–69, 72
trackballs, 10
tracking deleted files, 137–139
TSRs, memory for, 132–133

U

UNDELETE command,
  140–143

UNFORMAT command,
  143–146
upper memory, 129, 132–133

V

VER command, 3
vertical bars (|) for piping, 93,
  95–97
video mode for programs, 75
views, selecting, 77–78
virtual drives, 135–136
volume labels, 43, 65

W

wildcard characters, 27

X

XMS (extended memory), 75,
  129–131, 134–136

Common DOS Command Prompt Operations

■ ■ ■ ■ ■ ■ ■ ■ ■

■ Operation	■ Command	■ Step
Batch file (call)	CALL *filename*	10, 16
Batch file (create)	EDIT *filename*.BAT	16
Batch file (run)	*filename*	16
Clear screen	CLS	12
Date (change)	DATE	12
Directory (create)	MKDIR or MD	12
Directory (select)	CHDIR or CD	12
Directory (view)	TREE	12
Drive (select)	*drive*:	12
Edit file	EDIT *filename.ext*	15
Expanded memory (install)	DEVICE=EMM386.EXE	18
Extended memory (install)	DEVICE=HIMEM.SYS	18
Find text	FIND	13
Files (view)	DIR	12
Help	HELP [*command*]	12
High memory (use)	DOS=HIGH	18
Macros (create/use)	DOSKEY	7
Memory (view contents)	MEM	18
Partition hard disk	FDISK	19
Print file or output	PRINT or >PRN	13
Printer (configure)	MODE	17
Prompt (change)	PROMPT	17
RAM disk (install)	DEVICE=RAMDRIVE.SYS	18
Redirect output	>, <, >>	13
Reserved memory (install)	DOS=UMB	18
Reserved memory (use)	DEVICEHIGH,LOADHIGH	18
Run program	*program name*	5
Search for programs	PATH	17
Sort	SORT	13
Speed disk access	DEVICE=SMARTDRV.SYS	18
Speed file access	FASTOPEN	18
System tracks (copy)	SYS	6
Time (change)	TIME	12
Undelete file	UNDELETE	19
Unformat disk	UNFORMAT	19
Upper memory (install)	DOS=UMB	18
Upper memory (use)	DEVICEHIGH, LOADHIGH	18
Version (view)	VER	1